STECK-VAUGHN

LEVEL

G

Language

EXERCISES

STECK-VAUGHN
C O M P A N Y
A subsidiary of National Education Corporation

Acknowledgments

Senior Editor: Diane Sharpe
Project Editor: Stephanie Muller
Product Development: The Wheetley Company, Inc.
Cover Design: Sue Heatly Design

Macmillan Publishing Company: Pronunciation Key, reprinted with permission of the publisher, from *Macmillan School Dictionary 1.* Copyright © 1990 Macmillan Publishing Company, a division of Macmillan, Inc.

LANGUAGE EXERCISES Series:		
Level A/Pink	Level D/Gray	Level G/Gold
Level B/Orange	Level E/Red	Level H/Green
Level C/Violet	Level F/Blue	Review/Yellow

ISBN 0-8114-4196-2

14 15 PO 00 99 98 97 96 95 94 93

Table of Contents

UNIT 5 Composition

UNIT 6 Study Skills

Final Reviews

Synonyms and Antonyms

> ■ A **synonym** is a word that has the same or nearly the same meaning as one or more other words.   EXAMPLE: reply – response – answer

A. Write a synonym for each word below.

1. pleasant _____	**11.** nation _____	**21.** labor _____
2. enough _____	**12.** keep _____	**22.** finish _____
3. leave _____	**13.** quiet _____	**23.** different _____
4. inquire _____	**14.** trouble _____	**24.** little _____
5. fearless _____	**15.** begin _____	**25.** locate _____
6. artificial _____	**16.** purchase _____	**26.** difficult _____
7. famous _____	**17.** certain _____	**27.** vacant _____
8. trade _____	**18.** always _____	**28.** shout _____
9. house _____	**19.** positive _____	**29.** journey _____
10. simple _____	**20.** world _____	**30.** teach _____

> ■ An **antonym** is a word that has the opposite meaning of another word.   EXAMPLE: old – new

B. Write an antonym for each word below.

1. failure _____	**11.** stop _____	**21.** short _____
2. absent _____	**12.** raise _____	**22.** build _____
3. before _____	**13.** little _____	**23.** under _____
4. slow _____	**14.** help _____	**24.** always _____
5. all _____	**15.** busy _____	**25.** buy _____
6. forget _____	**16.** smooth _____	**26.** pretty _____
7. love _____	**17.** coarse _____	**27.** smile _____
8. no _____	**18.** east _____	**28.** happy _____
9. friend _____	**19.** quiet _____	**29.** light _____
10. early _____	**20.** rich _____	**30.** forward _____

Homonyms

> ■ A **homonym** is a word that sounds the same as another word but has a different spelling and a different meaning.
> EXAMPLES: aisle – I'll – isle   flower – flour

A. Write a homonym for each word below.

1. peace _____
2. altar _____
3. to _____
4. way _____
5. beech _____
6. plain _____
7. coarse _____
8. seem _____
9. knew _____
10. sale _____

11. sew _____
12. break _____
13. week _____
14. rein _____
15. bare _____
16. scene _____
17. mite _____
18. whole _____
19. hoarse _____
20. fourth _____

21. knight _____
22. hymn _____
23. through _____
24. grown _____
25. wrap _____
26. prey _____
27. strait _____
28. sole _____
29. hear _____
30. ware _____

B. Underline the correct homonym(s) in each sentence below.

1. The (two, too, to) people walked very slowly (passed, past) the house.
2. The children were (two, too, to) tired (two, too, to) talk.
3. Did you (hear, here) that noise?
4. Yes, I (heard, herd) it.
5. I do (knot, not) (know, no) of a person who is (knot, not) ready to help the hungry people of the world.
6. Michelle, you (seam, seem) to have forgotten about (our, hour) plans for the picnic.
7. Who (won, one) the citizenship (medal, meddle) this year?
8. Jim, how much do you (way, weigh)?
9. The night (air, heir) is (sew, so) cool that you will (knead, need) a light jacket.
10. The small plants were set out in orderly (rows, rose).
11. I (knew, new) those (knew, new) shoes would hurt my (feat, feet).
12. Which states lead in the production of (beat, beet) sugar?
13. We did (not, knot) go to the (seen, scene) of the wreck.
14. Sue wore the belt around her (waist, waste).

Homographs

■ A **homograph** is a word that has the same spelling as another word but a different meaning and sometimes a different pronunciation.
EXAMPLE: <u>saw</u>, meaning "have seen," and <u>saw</u>, meaning "a tool used for cutting"

A. Circle the letter for the definition that best defines each underlined homograph.

1. Sara jumped at the <u>bangs</u> of the exploding balloons.

   a. fringe of hair   **b.** loud noises

2. She grabbed a stick to <u>arm</u> herself against the threat.

   a. part of the body   **b.** take up a weapon

3. The dog's <u>bark</u> woke the family.

   a. noise a dog makes   **b.** outside covering on a tree

4. Mix the pancake <u>batter</u> for three minutes.

   a. person at bat   **b.** mixture for cooking

5. The <u>checkers</u> are working as fast as they can.

   a. pieces of a board game   **b.** people who check; cashiers

6. I promised to bring a <u>can</u> of beans to the party.

   a. metal container   **b.** able to

7. The chick's <u>down</u> was very soft.

   a. soft feathers   **b.** from a higher to a lower place

8. If you <u>desert</u> me here, I'll never get out.

   a. dry, sandy place   **b.** leave

9. <u>Duck</u> your head, and pour some water on your neck.

   a. water bird   **b.** lower the head

10. Be careful when you <u>alight</u> from the carriage.

    a. on fire   **b.** get down from

B. Write the homograph for each pair of meanings below. The first letter of each word is given for you.

1. **a.** building for horses   **b.** delay   s _____

2. **a.** a metal fastener   **b.** a sound made with fingers   s _____

3. **a.** to crush   **b.** a yellow vegetable   s _____

4. **a.** a bad doctor   **b.** the sound made by a duck   q _____

5. **a.** to strike   **b.** a party fruit drink   p _____

Prefixes

- A **prefix** added to the beginning of a base word changes the meaning of the word.

  EXAMPLE: dis-, meaning "opposite of," + the base word appear = disappear, meaning "the opposite of appear"

  EXAMPLES:

prefix	meaning	prefix	meaning
in-	not	re-	again
dis-	not	fore-	before
un-	not	pre-	before
trans-	across	mis-	wrong
		with-	from, against

- **Write a new word using one of the prefixes listed above. Then write the meaning of the new word.**

WORD	NEW WORD	MEANING
1. fair	_____	_____
2. justice	_____	_____
3. tell	_____	_____
4. warn	_____	_____
5. visible	_____	_____
6. spell	_____	_____
7. agree	_____	_____
8. see	_____	_____
9. behave	_____	_____
10. stand	_____	_____
11. complete	_____	_____
12. please	_____	_____
13. drawn	_____	_____
14. likely	_____	_____
15. match	_____	_____
16. clean	_____	_____
17. understand	_____	_____
18. correct	_____	_____

Suffixes

■ A **suffix** added to the end of a base word changes the meaning of the word.
  EXAMPLE: -less, meaning "without," + the base word <u>worth</u> = <u>worthless</u>,
  meaning "without worth"

  EXAMPLES:

suffix	meaning	suffix	meaning
-less	without	-ist	one skilled in
-ish	of the nature of	-tion	art of
-ous	full of	-ful	full of
-en	to make	-al	pertaining to
-hood	state of being	-able	able to be
-ward	in the direction of	-ible	able to be
-ness	quality of		

■ Sometimes you need to change the spelling of a base word when a
  suffix is added.
  EXAMPLE: happy – happiness

■ **Write a new word using one of the suffixes listed above. Then write the meaning of the new word.**

WORD	NEW WORD	MEANING
1. care	_____	_____
2. truth	_____	_____
3. fame	_____	_____
4. soft	_____	_____
5. down	_____	_____
6. light	_____	_____
7. east	_____	_____
8. honor	_____	_____
9. thank	_____	_____
10. rest	_____	_____
11. child	_____	_____
12. remark	_____	_____
13. violin	_____	_____
14. courage	_____	_____
15. worth	_____	_____

Contractions

> - A **contraction** is a word formed by joining two other words.
> - An **apostrophe** shows where a letter or letters have been omitted.
>   EXAMPLE: had not = hadn't
> - <u>Won't</u> is an exception.
>   EXAMPLE: will not = won't

A. Write the contraction for each pair of words.

1. did not _____
2. was not _____
3. we are _____
4. is not _____
5. who is _____
6. had not _____
7. I will _____
8. I am _____
9. it is _____
10. do not _____

11. they have _____
12. would not _____
13. will not _____
14. does not _____
15. were not _____
16. there is _____
17. could not _____
18. I have _____
19. she will _____
20. they are _____

B. Underline each contraction. Write the words that make up the contraction on the lines.

1. They're dusting the piano very carefully before they inspect it. _____

2. They'll want to look closely, in case there are any scratches. _____

3. If it's in good condition, Mary's parents will buy it for her. _____

4. Mary's an excellent piano player. _____

5. Her parents think she'll earn a college scholarship with her talent. _____

6. Tom doesn't play the piano, but he's a great cook. _____ _____

7. He'd like to be a professional chef. _____

8. His parents would've liked for him to go to college. _____

9. But they aren't concerned as long as Tom's happy. _____ _____

10. Tom and Mary think they've got very understanding parents. _____

Compound Words

> ■ A **compound word** is a word that is made up of two or more words. The meaning of many compound words is related to the meaning of each individual word.
>   EXAMPLE: blue + berry = blueberry, meaning "a type of berry that is blue in color"
> ■ Compound words may be written as one word, as hyphenated words, or as two separate words.
>   EXAMPLES: longhorn   long-term   long distance

A. Combine the words in the list to make compound words. You may use words more than once.

air	knob	door	port	paper	condition	black	berry
sand	line	stand	under	way	ground	bird	sea

1. _____

2. _____

3. _____

4. _____

5. _____

6. _____

7. _____

8. _____

9. _____

10. _____

11. _____

12. _____

B. Answer the following questions.

1. Whirl means "to move in circles." What is a whirlpool?

   _____

2. Since quick means "moves rapidly," what is quicksand?

   _____

3. Rattle means "to make sharp, short sounds quickly." What is a rattlesnake?

   _____

4. A ring is "a small, circular band." What is an earring?

   _____

5. Pool can mean "a group of people who do something together." What is a car pool?

   _____

6. A lace can be "a string or cord that is used to hold something together." What is a shoelace?

   _____

Connotation/Denotation

- The **denotation** of a word is its exact meaning as stated in a dictionary.
  EXAMPLE: The denotation of stingy is "ungenerous" or "miserly."
- The **connotation** of a word is an added meaning that suggests something positive or negative.
  EXAMPLES: **Negative:** Stingy suggests "ungenerous." Stingy has a negative connotation.
  Positive: Economical suggests "efficient" and "careful." Economical has a positive connotation.
- Some words are neutral. They do not suggest either good or bad feelings.
  EXAMPLES: garage, kitchen, roof

A. Write (−) if the underlined word has a negative connotation. Write (+) if it has a positive connotation. Write (N) if the word is neutral.

_____ 1. This is my house.

_____ 2. This is my home.

_____ 3. The club members discussed Harvey's problem.

_____ 4. The club members gossiped about Harvey's problem.

_____ 5. Our pet dog is sick.

_____ 6. Our pet dog is diseased.

_____ 7. The play was enjoyable.

_____ 8. The play was fantastic.

_____ 9. Julie is boring.

_____ 10. Julie is quiet.

B. Fill each blank with the word that suggests the connotation given.

1. Our experience of the storm was _____. (negative)

2. Our experience of the storm was _____. (positive)

3. Our experience of the storm was _____. (neutral)

| unpleasant |
| exciting |
| horrible |

4. Monica is _____. (neutral)

5. Monica is _____. (positive)

6. Monica is _____. (negative)

| old |
| over-the-hill |
| mature |

Idioms

> ■ An **idiom** is an expression that has a meaning different from the usual meanings of the individual words within it.
> EXAMPLE: <u>Lit a fire under me</u> means "got me going," not "burned me."

A. Underline the idiom in each sentence. Then write what the idiom means.

1. Kathy's mother blew her top when she saw Kathy's messy room.

   _____

2. Kathy said she had to hit the books for a test and didn't have time to clean.

   _____

3. Mom wanted Kathy to be able to kick up her heels at her surprise party, but first she needed help getting the house ready.

   _____

4. Since Kathy's mom didn't believe in beating around the bush, she told Kathy what was going on.

   _____

5. Even though Kathy's mom had to spill the beans about the party, Kathy was happy.

   _____

B. Underline each idiom. Then write one definition that tells the exact meaning of the phrase and another definition that tells what the phrase means in the sentence.

1. When I finish the test, I'm going to hit the road.

   a. ___Pound on the street_____

   b. ___Leave_____

2. I had to eat crow when I found out I was wrong about the test date.

   a. _____

   b. _____

3. With final exams coming, I'll have to burn the midnight oil.

   a. _____

   b. _____

4. I thought I was so smart, but that test really cut me down to size.

   a. _____

   b. _____

A. Write <u>S</u> before each pair of synonyms. Write <u>A</u> before each set of antonyms. Write <u>HM</u> before each set of homonyms. Write <u>HG</u> before each set of homographs.

_____ 1. quiet, noisy   _____ 5. wind, wind   _____ 9. healthy, sick

_____ 2. ate, eight   _____ 6. begin, start   _____ 10. fly, fly

_____ 3. fearless, brave   _____ 7. gentle, rough   _____ 11. road, rode

_____ 4. tear, tear   _____ 8. piece, peace   _____ 12. calm, peaceful

B. Underline the pair of words that can be written as a contraction in each sentence. Then write each contraction on the line.

_____ 1. Yolanda does not want to work late today.

_____ 2. She would rather come in early tomorrow.

_____ 3. It is getting dark.

_____ 4. She does not like driving in the dark.

_____ 5. You must not blame her.

_____ 6. Who is going to stay with her?

_____ 7. James did not volunteer.

C. Choose an appropriate prefix or suffix from the box for each of the underlined words below. Write the new word on the line.

dis-	mis-	re-	un-	-ish	-ful	-less	-en

1. full of <u>thanks</u> _____   5. to make <u>black</u> in color _____

2. to <u>pay</u> again _____   6. without <u>thanks</u> _____

3. to not <u>agree</u> _____   7. not <u>happy</u> _____

4. act as a <u>fool</u> _____   8. <u>take</u> wrongly _____

D. Write (–) if the underlined word has a negative connotation. Write (+) if the underlined word has a positive connotation.

_____ 1. Joe is sometimes <u>narrowminded</u>.   _____ 6. The child <u>grabbed</u> the toy and ran away.

_____ 2. Marie is very <u>outgoing</u>.   _____ 7. Those insects are real <u>pests</u>.

_____ 3. Do you like <u>gossip</u>?   _____ 8. I <u>demand</u> that you listen to me.

_____ 4. Carla can <u>gab</u> for hours.   _____ 9. The <u>mansion</u> was very old.

_____ 5. Let's <u>donate</u> this later.   _____ 10. Steve drives an old <u>jalopy</u>.

Using What You've Learned

A. On the line before each sentence, write <u>synonym</u>, <u>antonym</u>, <u>homonym</u>, or <u>homograph</u> to describe the pair of underlined words.

_____ 1. You may give an <u>answer</u>, but be sure of your <u>reply</u>.

_____ 2. <u>Be</u> very careful in your explanation of the <u>bee</u>.

_____ 3. The <u>bank</u> on the river <u>bank</u> refused my request for a loan.

_____ 4. I <u>ate</u> dinner at <u>eight</u> last night.

_____ 5. <u>Look</u> in the closet to <u>see</u> if my protective suit is there.

_____ 6. Randy knew the <u>answer</u> to the <u>question</u> about bee colonies.

_____ 7. Why are you making such a <u>big</u> fuss over such a <u>little</u> thing as a bee sting?

B. In each sentence, underline the word that contains a prefix or a suffix. Then write a definition of that word.

1. Harry was thankful for a chance to play.

   _____

2. Connie was very unhappy about missing the ball.

   _____

3. The coach was displeased at our performance.

   _____

4. It was a thankless job, but someone had to clean up the park.

   _____

5. We repainted the bleachers this summer.

   _____

6. We will transplant flower bulbs this fall.

   _____

7. We were unsure that it would be done by Saturday.

   _____

C. Write the words that make up each contraction below.

1. won't _____   3. it's _____   5. she'll _____

2. I'm _____   4. weren't _____   6. we're _____

D. Write (−) if the definition has a negative connotation. Write (N) if the definition is neutral.

1. **desert** _____ leave _____ abandon

2. **curious** _____ nosy; prying _____ eager to know

3. **clown** _____ circus performer _____ silly actor

4. **jungle** _____ hectic, crowded place _____ place with much plant growth

5. **anxious** _____ concerned _____ nervous; full of fear

6. **fall** _____ drop _____ plunge

7. **look** _____ view _____ stare, gawk

8. **response** _____ excuse _____ explanation

E. Rewrite the paragraph. Replace the idioms with other words or phrases that have the same meaning as the idioms.

"I'd take the rumor about the test with a grain of salt," Tom said. "Mrs. Jason knows we're on top of the world about the class party. I'm sure she wouldn't knock the pins out from under us by making us hit the books now for a test. We've been trying to find out, but she hasn't spilled the beans yet. Maybe we'd better stop beating around the bush and ask her. I'd hate to end up just taking a shot in the dark on an important test."

_____

_____

_____

_____

_____

_____

_____

_____

_____

_____

_____

_____

_____

> ■ A **sentence** is a group of words that expresses a complete thought.
> EXAMPLE: We found a deserted cabin at the top of the hill.

■ **Some of the following groups of words are sentences, and some are not. Write <u>S</u> before each group that is a sentence. Punctuate each sentence with a period.**

_____ 1. Tomás did not go to the auto show____

_____ 2. By the side of the babbling brook____

_____ 3. I went to the new museum last week____

_____ 4. Mile after mile along the great highway____

_____ 5. Check all work carefully____

_____ 6. Down the narrow aisle of the church____

_____ 7. I have lost my hat____

_____ 8. On our way to work this morning____

_____ 9. Leontyne Price, a famous singer____

_____ 10. We saw Katherine and Sheryl yesterday____

_____ 11. The severe cold of last winter____

_____ 12. Once upon a time, long, long ago____

_____ 13. There was a gorgeous sunset last night____

_____ 14. He ran home____

_____ 15. My brother and my sister____

_____ 16. Tom and Matt did a great job____

_____ 17. We saw a beaver in the deep ravine____

_____ 18. The cat in our neighbor's yard____

_____ 19. Every year at the state fair____

_____ 20. As we came to the sharp curve in the road____

_____ 21. Just before we were ready____

_____ 22. I heard that you and Doug have a new paper route____

_____ 23. Longfellow is called the children's poet____

_____ 24. Into the parking garage____

_____ 25. We washed and waxed the truck____

_____ 26. Through the door and up the stairs____

_____ 27. As quickly as possible____

_____ 28. We saw the new killer whale at the zoo____

_____ 29. John parked the car on the street____

_____ 30. We had ice cream and fruit for dessert____

> - A **declarative sentence** makes a statement. It is followed by a period (.). EXAMPLE: Alicia is my cousin.
> - An **interrogative sentence** asks a question. It is followed by a question mark (?). EXAMPLE: Where are you going?
> - An **imperative sentence** expresses a command or request. It is followed by a period (.). EXAMPLE: Close the door.
> - An **exclamatory sentence** expresses strong emotion. It can also express a command or request that is made with great excitement. It is followed by an exclamation mark (!). EXAMPLES: How you frightened me! Look at that accident!

A. Write D for declarative, IN for interrogative, IM for imperative, or E for exclamatory before each sentence. Put the correct punctuation at the end of each sentence.

_____ 1. Everyone will be here by nine o'clock____

_____ 2. Train your mind to do its work efficiently____

_____ 3. How does a canal lock work____

_____ 4. Prepare each day's assignment on time____

_____ 5. Are we going to the game now____

_____ 6. Who brought these delicious peaches____

_____ 7. Our guests have arrived____

_____ 8. What is meant by rotation of crops____

_____ 9. Please bring a glass of water____

_____ 10. Stop that noise____

_____ 11. Always stand erect____

_____ 12. Who arranged these flowers____

_____ 13. Anna, what do you have in that box____

_____ 14. The Vikings were famous sailors____

_____ 15. Have you solved all the problems in our lesson____

_____ 16. Diego, hand me that wrench____

_____ 17. What is the capital of California____

_____ 18. Cultivate a pleasant manner____

_____ 19. How is a pizza made____

_____ 20. Block that kick____

_____ 21. A nation is measured by the character of its people____

_____ 22. Are you an early riser____

_____ 23. Practice good table manners____

_____ 24. What a wonderful time we've had____

_____ 25. How did you get here so early____

_____ 26. Look out for those cars____

_____ 27. Take good care of my dog____

_____ 28. There are many cotton mills in our state____

_____ 29. Name the capital of Nevada____

_____ 30. Hurrah, the game is over____

_____ 31. Draw a map of the United States____

_____ 32. Geysers were first discovered in Iceland____

_____ 33. Have you ever been on a roller coaster____

_____ 34. Sweep the front walk____

_____ 35. Do not measure people by what they have____

_____ 36. A great nation is made only by worthy citizens____

_____ 37. Anna Moffo has sung with many of the major opera companies____

_____ 38. What is the longest river in our state____

_____ 39. Oh, you have a new car____

_____ 40. Andrea, why weren't you at the meeting____

_____ 41. The organization will elect officers tomorrow____

_____ 42. Chris, I have a long piece of twine____

_____ 43. Paul, jump quickly____

B. **Only one group of words in each pair below is a sentence. Circle the sentence, and tell what kind it is. Write D for declarative, IN for interrogative, IM for imperative, or E for exclamatory.**

_____ 1. When will the train arrive? Two hours late.

_____ 2. It is delayed by bad weather. Not here yet.

_____ 3. From California. My grandparents are on it.

_____ 4. I haven't seen them in two years! Am waiting patiently.

_____ 5. Enjoy traveling. They will stay with us for two weeks.

_____ 6. We have many things planned for them. A good visit.

_____ 7. Sleep in the guest room. To our city's new zoo?

_____ 8. Grandpa used to work at a zoo. Many animals.

_____ 9. Go in the reptile house. Took care of the elephants.

_____ 10. Each elephant had a name. Wally, Sandra, and Joe.

_____ 11. The elephants liked to train with Grandpa. Good job.

_____ 12. Sandra, the elephant, had a baby. In the zoo.

_____ 13. Male elephant. What did the zoo officials name the baby?

_____ 14. People in the zoo. They surprised my grandpa!

_____ 15. He never had an elephant named for him before! Seal exhibit.

Complete Subjects and Predicates

> - Every sentence has two main parts, a **complete subject** and a **complete predicate.**
> - The complete subject includes all the words that tell who or what the sentence is about.   EXAMPLE: **All chickadees**/hunt insect eggs.
> - The complete predicate includes all the words that state the action or condition of the subject.   EXAMPLE: All chickadees/**hunt insect eggs.**

A. Draw a line between the complete subject and the complete predicate in each sentence below.

1. Amy/built a bird feeder for the backyard.

2. This cleaner will remove paint.

3. Many beautiful waltzes were composed by Johann Strauss.

4. Queen Victoria ruled England for many years.

5. Eighty people are waiting in line for tickets.

6. Mario's last visit was during the summer.

7. The rocket was soon in orbit.

8. Our last meeting was held in my living room.

9. The farmers are harvesting their wheat.

10. Our new house has six rooms.

11. The heart pumps blood throughout the body.

12. This computer will help you work faster.

13. My best friend has moved to Santa Fe, New Mexico.

14. A deep silence fell upon the crowd.

15. The police officers were stopping the speeding motorists.

16. The French chef prepared excellent food.

17. My father is a mechanic.

18. José Salazar is running for the city council.

19. Lightning struck a tree in our yard.

20. Magazines about bicycling are becoming increasingly popular.

21. They answered every question honestly during the interview.

22. The gray twilight came before the program ended.

23. Steve has a way with words.

24. That section of the state has many pine forests.

25. We will have a party for Teresa on Friday.

26. Butterflies flew around the flowers.

27. The heavy bus was stuck in the mud.

B. Write a sentence by adding a complete predicate to each complete subject.

1. All of the students _____

2. Elephants _____

3. The top of the mountain _____

4. The television programs tonight _____

5. I _____

6. Each of the girls _____

7. My father's truck _____

8. The dam across the river _____

9. Our new station wagon _____

10. You _____

11. The books in our bookcase _____

12. The mountains _____

13. Today's paper _____

14. The magazine staff _____

C. Write a sentence by adding a complete subject to each complete predicate.

1. _____ is the largest city in Mexico.

2. _____ came to our program.

3. _____ is a valuable mineral.

4. _____ grow beside the road.

5. _____ traveled day and night.

6. _____ was a great inventor.

7. _____ wrote the letter of complaint.

8. _____ met us at the airport.

9. _____ made ice cream for the picnic.

10. _____ made a nest in our tree.

11. _____ lives near the shopping center.

12. _____ have a meeting on Saturday.

Simple Subjects and Predicates

> ■ The **simple subject** of a sentence is the main word in the complete subject. The simple subject is a noun or a pronoun. Sometimes the simple subject is also the complete subject.   EXAMPLES: Our **car**/swayed in the strong wind. **Cars**/sway in the strong wind.

A. Draw a line between the complete subject and the complete predicate in each sentence below. Then underline the simple subject.

1. The plants sprouted quickly after the first rain.
2. The television program was very informative.
3. I used a word processor to write the paper.
4. My father's truck is parked in the driveway.
5. The beavers created a dam in the river.
6. The books lined the shelves like toy soldiers.
7. Hail pounded against the storm door.
8. My new bicycle is a ten-speed.
9. My favorite subject is history.
10. The colorful bird sang a beautiful melody.
11. The tree trunk was about five feet in diameter.
12. The sidewalk had cracks in the pavement.

> ■ The **simple predicate** of a sentence is a verb within the complete predicate. The simple predicate may be made up of one word or more than one word.   EXAMPLES: Our car/**swayed**. The wind/**was blowing** hard.

B. In each sentence below, draw a line between the complete subject and the complete predicate. Underline the simple predicate twice.

1. A rare Chinese vase was on display.
2. Many of the children had played.
3. All of the group went on a hike.
4. He drove the bus slowly over the slippery pavement.
5. A large number of water-skiers were on the lake last Saturday.
6. Birds have good eyesight.
7. Who discovered the Pacific Ocean?
8. I am reading the assignment now.
9. The glare of the headlights blinded us.
10. The problem on the next page is harder.

Position of Subjects

> - When the subject of a sentence comes before the verb, the sentence is in **natural order.** EXAMPLE: Maria went home.
> - When the verb or part of the verb comes before the subject, the sentence is in **inverted order.** EXAMPLES: On the branch were two birds.
>   There are four children in my family. Here is my friend.
> - Many questions are in inverted order. EXAMPLE: Where is Jim?
> - Sometimes the subject of a sentence is not expressed, as in a command or request. The understood subject is you. EXAMPLES: Bring the sandwiches. (You) bring the sandwiches.

- **Rewrite each inverted sentence in natural order. Rewrite commands or requests by including you as the subject. Then underline each simple subject once and each simple predicate twice in each sentence you write.**

1. Where was the sunken treasure ship?

   The sunken treasure ship was where?
   _____

2. Beyond the bridge were several sailboats.

   _____

3. There is no one in that room.

   _____

4. From the gymnasium came the shouts of the victorious team.

   _____

5. Beside the walk grew beautiful flowers.

   _____

6. When is the graduation party?

   _____

7. Bring your sales report to the meeting.

   _____

8. There were only three floats in the parade.

   _____

9. From the yard came the bark of a dog.

   _____

10. Place the forks to the left of the plate.

   _____

Compound Subjects

> ■ A **compound subject** is made up of two or more simple subjects.
> EXAMPLE: **Henri** and **Milly**/are tall people.

A. Draw a line between the complete subject and the complete predicate in each sentence. Write <u>SS</u> for a simple subject. Write <u>CS</u> for a compound subject.

<u> CS </u> **1.** Arturo and I/often work late on Friday.

_____ **2.** Sandy left the person near the crowded exit.

_____ **3.** She and I will mail the packages to San Francisco today.

_____ **4.** Detroit and Chicago are two cities visited by the group.

_____ **5.** The fire spread rapidly to other buildings in the neighborhood.

_____ **6.** Luis and Susan helped their parents with the chores.

_____ **7.** Swimming, jogging, and hiking were our favorite sports.

_____ **8.** Melbourne and Sydney are important Australian cities.

_____ **9.** Eric and I had an interesting experience Saturday.

_____ **10.** The Red Sea and the Mediterranean Sea are connected by the Suez Canal.

_____ **11.** The Republicans and the Democrats made many speeches before the election.

_____ **12.** The people waved to us from the top of the cliff.

_____ **13.** Liz and Jim crated the freshly-picked apples.

_____ **14.** Clean clothes and a neat appearance are important in an interview.

_____ **15.** The kitten and the old dog are good friends.

_____ **16.** David and Paul are on their way to the swimming pool.

_____ **17.** Tom combed his dog's shiny black coat.

_____ **18.** Redbud and dogwood trees bloom in the spring.

_____ **19.** I hummed a cheerful tune on the way to the meeting.

_____ **20.** Buffalo, deer, and antelope once roamed the plains.

_____ **21.** Linda and Jim raked the leaves.

_____ **22.** Chicago and Springfield are two cities in Illinois.

_____ **23.** Hang gliding is a popular sport in Hawaii.

_____ **24.** Our class went on a field trip to the aquarium.

_____ **25.** The doctor asked him to get a blood test.

B. Write two sentences containing compound subjects.

1. _____

2. _____

Compound Predicates

> ■ A **compound predicate** is made up of two or more simple predicates.
> EXAMPLE: Esther/**dances** and **sings.**

A. Draw a line between the complete subject and the complete predicate in each sentence. Write <u>SP</u> for each simple predicate. Write <u>CP</u> for each compound predicate.

<u>CP</u>   **1.** Eddie/grinned and nodded.

_____   **2.** Plants need air to live.

_____   **3.** Old silver tea kettles were among their possessions.

_____   **4.** My aunt buys and sells real estate.

_____   **5.** Snow covered every highway in the county.

_____   **6.** Mr. Sanders designs and makes odd pieces of furniture.

_____   **7.** Popcorn is one of my favorite snack foods.

_____   **8.** Football is one of my favorite sports.

_____   **9.** The ducks quickly crossed the road and found the ducklings.

_____   **10.** They came early and stayed late.

_____   **11.** Crystal participated in the Special Olympics this year.

_____   **12.** José raked and sacked the leaves.

_____   **13.** Perry built the fire and cooked supper.

_____   **14.** We collected old newspapers for the recycling center.

_____   **15.** Doug arrived in Cincinnati during the afternoon.

_____   **16.** Tony's parents are visiting in Oregon and Washington.

_____   **17.** The Garzas live in that apartment building on Oak Street.

_____   **18.** The shingles were picked up and delivered today.

_____   **19.** The audience talked and laughed before the performance.

_____   **20.** Automobiles crowd and jam that highway early in the morning.

_____   **21.** The apples are rotting in the boxes.

_____   **22.** The leader of the group grumbled and scolded.

_____   **23.** She worked hard and waited patiently.

_____   **24.** Benjamin Franklin was a great American.

_____   **25.** The supervisor has completed the work for the week.

B. Write two sentences containing compound predicates.

1. _____

2. _____

Combining Sentences

> - Two sentences in which the subjects are different and the predicates are the same can be combined into one sentence. The two subjects are joined by and.   EXAMPLE: **Hurricanes** are storms. **Tornadoes** are storms. **Hurricanes and tornadoes** are storms.
> - Two sentences in which the subjects are the same and the predicates are different can be combined into one sentence. The two predicates may be joined by or, and, or but.   EXAMPLE: Hurricanes **begin over tropical oceans.** Hurricanes **move inland.** Hurricanes **begin over tropical oceans and move inland.**

- **Combine each pair of sentences below. Underline the compound subject or the compound predicate in each sentence that you write.**

1. Lightning is part of a thunderstorm. Thunder is part of a thunderstorm.

   _____

2. Thunderstorms usually happen in the spring. Thunderstorms bring heavy rains.

   _____

3. Depending on how close or far away it is, thunder sounds like a sharp crack. Depending on how close or far away it is, thunder rumbles.

   _____

   _____

4. Lightning is very exciting to watch. Lightning can be very dangerous.

   _____

5. Lightning causes many fires. Lightning harms many people.

   _____

6. An open field is an unsafe place to be during a thunderstorm. A golf course is an unsafe place to be during a thunderstorm.

   _____

   _____

7. Benjamin Franklin wanted to protect people from lightning. Benjamin Franklin invented the lightning rod.

   _____

   _____

8. A lightning rod is a metal rod placed on the top of a building. A lightning rod is connected to the ground by a cable.

   _____

   _____

Direct Objects

> ■ The **direct object** tells who or what receives the action of the verb. The direct object is a noun or pronoun that follows an action verb.
>
> EXAMPLE: You told the **truth.**
> (DO above **truth**)

■ **Underline the verb in each sentence. Then write DO above each direct object.**

1. Elephants <u>can carry</u> logs with their trunks.
   (DO above logs)

2. Who made this magazine rack?

3. Do you always plan a daily schedule?

4. They easily won the game.

5. Father baked an apple pie for dinner.

6. Who tuned your piano?

7. I take guitar lessons once a week.

8. Who composed this melody?

9. I especially enjoy mystery stories.

10. The astronauts orbited the earth many times.

11. I bought this coat in New York.

12. Did he find his glasses?

13. Anne drove the truck to the hardware store.

14. The boy shrugged his shoulders.

15. We have finished our work today.

16. We drink milk for breakfast.

17. She can solve any problem quickly.

18. Who made our first flag?

19. You will learn something from this lesson.

20. Every person needs friends.

21. I have found a dime.

22. Jim ate an apple for a snack.

Indirect Objects

> ■ The **indirect object** is the noun or pronoun that tells to whom or for whom an action is done. In order to have an indirect object, a sentence must have a direct object.
> ■ The indirect object is usually placed between the action verb and the direct object.
>
>   EXAMPLE: Who sold **you** that fantastic **bike?**
>   (IO above **you**, DO above **bike**)

■ **Underline the verb in each sentence. Then write DO above the direct object and IO above the indirect object.**

1. Certain marine plants <u>give</u> the Red Sea (IO) its (DO) color.

2. Grandmother gave me a check for twenty dollars.

3. The magician showed the audience a few of her tricks.

4. The coach taught them the rules of the game.

5. Roberto brought us some foreign coins.

6. This interesting book will give every reader pleasure.

7. Have you written your brother a letter?

8. They made us some sandwiches to take on our hike.

9. The astronaut gave Mission Control the data.

10. I bought my mother an etching at the art exhibit.

11. Hector, did you sell Mike your car?

12. We have given the dog a thorough scrubbing.

13. Give the usher your ticket.

14. Uncle Carl brought my brother a gold ring from Mexico.

15. Hand me a pencil, please.

16. The conductor gave the orchestra a short break.

17. Show me the picture of your boat.

18. I have given you my money.

19. Give Lee this message.

20. The club gave the town a new statue.

Independent and Subordinate Clauses

> - A **clause** is a group of words that contains a subject and a predicate. There are two kinds of clauses: **independent clauses** and **subordinate clauses.**
> - An **independent clause** can stand alone as a sentence because it expresses a complete thought.
>   EXAMPLE: **The students came in** when the bell rang. **The students came in.**

A. Underline the independent clause in each sentence below.

1. Frank will be busy because he is studying.

2. I have only one hour that I can spare.

3. The project must be finished when I get back.

4. Martha volunteered to do the typing that needs to be done.

5. The work is going too slowly for us to finish on time.

6. Before Ralph started to help, I didn't think we could finish.

7. What else should we do before we relax?

8. Since you forgot to give this page to Martha, you can type it.

9. After she had finished typing, we completed the project.

10. We actually got it finished before the deadline.

> - A **subordinate clause** has a subject and predicate but cannot stand alone as a sentence because it does not express a complete thought. A subordinate clause must be combined with an independent clause to make a sentence.
>   EXAMPLE: The stamp **that I bought** was already in my collection.

B. Underline the subordinate clause in each sentence below.

1. The people who went shopping found a great sale.

2. Tony's bike, which is a ten-speed, came from that store.

3. Juana was sad when the sale was over.

4. Marianne was excited because she wanted some new things.

5. Thomas didn't find anything since he went late.

6. The mall where we went shopping was new.

7. The people who own the stores are proud of the beautiful setting.

8. The mall, which is miles away, is serviced by the city bus.

9. We ran as fast as we could because the bus was coming.

10. We were panting because we had run fast.

Adjective Clauses

> ■ An **adjective clause** is a subordinate clause that modifies a noun or a
> pronoun. It answers the adjective question Which one? or What kind?
> It usually modifies the word directly preceding it. Most adjective clauses
> begin with a **relative pronoun**. A relative pronoun relates an adjective
> clause to the noun or pronoun that the clause modifies. Who, whose,
> which, and that are relative pronouns.
>   EXAMPLE: The coat **that I bought** was on sale.
>   noun   adjective clause

A. Underline the adjective clause in each sentence below.

1. A compass has a needle that always points northward.

2. A seismograph is an instrument that measures earthquake tremors.

3. Students who work in science laboratories today have a broad field of study.

4. This will be the first time that she has played in that position.

5. Jay is the boy whose wrist was broken.

6. The fish that I caught was large.

7. A sentence that contains a subordinate clause is a complex sentence.

8. Here is the photograph that I promised to show you.

9. The book that I read was very humorous.

B. Add an adjective clause to each independent clause below.

1. A microscope is an instrument   (that) _____

   _____

2. Patrick Henry was an American patriot   (who) _____

   _____

3. We have football players   (who) _____

   _____

4. They built a helicopter   (which) _____

   _____

5. Bunny is a dog   (that) _____

   _____

6. A telescope is an instrument   (that) _____

   _____

Adverb Clauses

- An **adverb clause** is a subordinate clause that modifies a verb, an adjective, or another adverb. It answers the adverb question How? Under what condition? or Why? Words that introduce adverb clauses are called **subordinating conjunctions.** The many subordinating conjunctions include such words as when, after, before, since, although, and because.   EXAMPLE: I finished **before the bell rang.**
  adverb clause

A. Underline the adverb clause in each sentence below.

1. Helen Keller was not blind when she was born.

2. Although she became blind, she attended college.

3. She received her college degree after she studied many hours.

4. Blind people can enjoy many books because they are printed in Braille.

5. When a person is blind, his or her family also needs help.

6. Family members can meet with experts before they change their home to help the blind person.

7. After they meet, family members and the blind person can live together more easily.

8. Although a person is blind, he or she can work.

9. Since blind people are otherwise capable, they can work in a variety of jobs.

10. After blind people receive training, they can work with computers.

B. Add an adverb clause to each independent clause below.

1. We ate breakfast   (before) _____

   _____

2. Jay and I carried umbrellas   (since) _____

   _____

3. We took the bus to the museum   (because) _____

   _____

4. People in line waited   (when) _____

   _____

5. We saw the exhibit   (after) _____

   _____

6. Joel and I baked cookies   (when) _____

   _____

Simple and Compound Sentences

> - A **simple sentence** contains only one independent clause. The subject, the predicate, or both may be compound.
>   - EXAMPLES: The courthouse/is the oldest building in town. Gale and Louise/are making costumes and dressing up.
> - A **compound sentence** consists of two or more independent clauses. Each independent clause in a compound sentence can stand alone as a separate sentence. The independent clauses are usually joined by <u>and</u>, <u>but</u>, <u>so</u>, <u>or</u>, <u>for</u>, or <u>yet</u> and a comma.
>   - EXAMPLE: Jack brought the chairs, but Mary forgot the extra table.
> - Sometimes a **semicolon (;)** is used to join two independent clauses in a compound sentence.
>   - EXAMPLE: The music started; the dance had begun.

A. Write <u>S</u> before each simple sentence, and write <u>CS</u> before each compound sentence.

_____ 1. We can wait for James, or we can go on ahead.

_____ 2. The carnival will start today in the empty lot.

_____ 3. Jack and Manuel are going to meet us there at six o'clock.

_____ 4. I really want to go to the carnival, yet I am not sure about going tonight.

_____ 5. I didn't mean to hurt Carl's feelings by not going.

_____ 6. You wait for the package, and I'll meet you at the carnival.

_____ 7. I can't skip my homework to go, but maybe I'll finish it this afternoon.

_____ 8. Jan and Suzanne are both working at the carnival this year.

B. Put brackets ([ ]) around the independent clauses in each compound sentence. Then underline the word or punctuation used to join the clauses.

1. You must observe all the rules, or you must withdraw from the race.

2. I did well on the test, and Maria did well, too.

3. Shall I carry this box, or do you want it to stay here?

4. We must closely guard our freedom, or an enemy will take it from us.

5. He threw a beautiful pass, but no one caught it.

6. The doctor treated the cut, but he did not have to make any stitches.

7. I like to spend weekends at home, but the others prefer to travel.

8. The year is almost over, and everyone is thinking of the new year.

9. The Pilgrims faced every hardship, yet they were thankful for every blessing.

10. Move the box over here; I'll unpack it.

11. Connie likes football; James prefers baseball.

12. I drive safely, but I always make everyone fasten seat belts.

13. Please get the telephone number, and I'll call after work.

Complex Sentences

24

> ■ A **complex sentence** contains one independent clause and one or more subordinate clauses.
>
> EXAMPLE: The person **who helps me carry these** gets some dessert.
> subordinate clause

A. Put brackets around the subordinate clause, and underline the independent clause in each complex sentence below.

1. <u>The shadows</u> [that had fallen between the trees] <u>were a deep purple</u>.

2. The soldiers waded across the stream where the water was shallow.

3. They waited for me until the last bus came.

4. The fans of that team were sad when the team lost the game.

5. When my uncle was here, he was charmed by the beauty of the hills.

6. Georgia will call for you when she is ready.

7. Some spiders that are found in Sumatra have legs seventeen inches long.

8. Those who are going will arrive on time.

9. Do not throw the bat after you've hit the ball.

10. Tell us about the trip that you made a year ago.

B. Add a subordinate clause that begins with the word in parentheses to make a complex sentence.

1. I try not to drive   (where) _____

_____

2. The electric light is an important invention   (that) _____

_____

3. The telephone stopped ringing   (before) _____

_____

4. He is the man   (who) _____

_____

5. This is the book   (that) _____

_____

6. Turn to the left   (when) _____

_____

Correcting Run-on Sentences

- Two or more independent clauses that are run together without the correct punctuation are called a **run-on sentence.**
  - EXAMPLE: The music was deafening I turned down the volume control.
- One way to correct a run-on sentence is to separate it into two sentences.
  - EXAMPLE: The music was deafening. I turned down the volume control.
- Another way to correct a run-on sentence is to make it into a compound sentence.
  - EXAMPLE: The music was deafening, so I turned down the volume control.
- Another way to correct a run-on sentence is to use a semicolon.
  - EXAMPLE: The music was deafening; I turned down the volume control.

- **Correct each run-on sentence below by writing it as two sentences or as a compound sentence.**

1. The student council held a meeting a meeting is held every month.

   _____

   _____

2. The council members are elected by the student body the student body is two thousand strong.

   _____

   _____

3. There is one council member from each homeroom, the president is elected by the council members.

   _____

   _____

4. Those who run for office must give speeches, the speeches should be short.

   _____

   _____

5. The council decides on many activities every activity idea is voted on.

   _____

   _____

6. Money is needed for many of the special activities, the council also plans fund-raisers in the school.

   _____

   _____

7. The annual school picnic is sponsored by the student council the picnic is in May.

   _____

   _____

Unit 2, Sentences

Expanding Sentences

- Sentences can be **expanded** by adding details to make them clearer and more interesting.   EXAMPLE: The children laughed. The **excited** children **in the circus tent** laughed **loudly.**
- Details added to sentences may answer these questions: When? Where? How? How often? To what degree? What kind? Which? How many?

A. Expand each sentence below by adding details to answer the questions shown in parentheses. Write the expanded sentence on the line.

1. The car stalled.   (What kind? Where?)

   _____

2. Mary raised the hood.   (How? Which?)

   _____

3. Smoke billowed from the engine.   (What kind? Where?)

   _____

4. She called the service station.   (When? Which?)

   _____

5. The phone rang.   (Which? How often?)

   _____

B. Decide how each of the following sentences can be expanded. Write your expanded sentence on the line.

1. The runner crossed the finish line.

   _____

2. The crowd cheered.

   _____

3. The reporter interviewed her.

   _____

4. She answered.

   _____

5. Her coach ran up to her.

   _____

6. She and her coach walked off the track.

   _____

7. She was awarded the medal.

   _____

A. Label each sentence as follows: Write **D** for declarative, **IN** for interrogative, **IM** for imperative, or **E** for exclamatory. Punctuate each sentence correctly.

_____ **1.** Did you forget our appointment___

_____ **2.** Be careful___

_____ **3.** All members will meet in this room___

_____ **4.** Help, I'm frightened___

_____ **5.** Where are you going___

_____ **6.** Oh, look out___

_____ **7.** Julie ran two miles___

_____ **8.** Place the books here___

B. In each sentence below, underline the words that are identified in parentheses.

1. (complete subject)   The lights around the public square went out.

2. (simple subject)   Stations are in all parts of our country.

3. (direct object)   Carol collects fans for a hobby.

4. (complete predicate)   We drove slowly across the bridge.

5. (simple predicate)   We saw an unusual flower.

6. (compound predicate)   Bill swims and dives quite well.

7. (compound subject)   The cake and bread are kept in the box.

8. (indirect object)   The referee gave our team a fifteen-yard penalty.

9. (direct object)   A good citizen obeys the laws, but a bad citizen doesn't.

10. (indirect object)   Please lend me your raincoat, so I can stay dry.

C. Write **CP** after each compound sentence and **CX** after each complex sentence.

1. The food that is needed will be bought. _____

2. Mary will get lettuce, but we may have some. _____

3. Jack, who said he would help, is late. _____

4. We will go, and they will meet us. _____

5. Jack will drive his car after it has been repaired. _____

6. We are going to Hay Park since it is on a lake. _____

7. There are canoes that can be rented. _____

D. Expand each sentence by adding details.

Dr. Peters ran. He had created a monster.

_____

_____

A. Read the sentences in the box. Then answer the questions below.

> **A.** Did I give you the tickets for the show?
> **B.** The sound track is fantastic!
> **C.** Be at my house by seven o'clock.
> **D.** You and I can ride downtown together.
> **E.** We can stop and eat before the show.

1. _____ Which sentence has a compound subject?
2. _____ Which sentence has a compound predicate?
3. _____ Which sentence has a direct object?
4. _____ Which sentence has an indirect object?

5. _____ Which sentence is interrogative?
6. _____ Which sentences are declarative?
7. _____ Which sentence is exclamatory?
8. _____ Which sentence is imperative?

9. What is the complete subject of E? _____

10. What is the simple subject of E? _____

11. What is the complete predicate of C? _____

B. Underline the independent clause, and circle the subordinate clause in each complex sentence below.

1. The streamers sagged after we hung them.

2. Mark knows party planning because he has lots of parties.

3. Everyone who wants to go to the party must bring something.

4. If everyone brings something, the party will be great.

5. Unless I am wrong, the party is tomorrow.

6. As if everything had been done, Jake ran out of the room.

7. The girls who planned the party received roses.

8. I will never forget the day that I fell on my face at a party.

C. Combine each pair of sentences below to form a compound sentence.

1. The team sat in the dugout. The fans sat in the stands.

   _____

2. The rain finally stopped. The game continued.

   _____

3. It was the bottom of the ninth inning. There were two outs.

   _____

4. The batter swung at the pitch. The umpire called, "Strike three!"

   _____

D. Rewrite each inverted sentence in natural order.

1. On the rocks perched two seagulls.

   _____

2. Here are the supplies for the classroom.

   _____

E. Create complex sentences by adding a subordinate clause or an independent clause to each group of words below.

1. He turned down the lonely road _____

2. When night came, _____

3. This was the site _____

4. After he looked around, _____

5. He continued to drive _____

6. When he got to the inn, _____

F. Rewrite the paragraph below, correcting the run-on sentences.

> Patty didn't know what to do, she had a terrible problem and she was trying to solve it. No matter how hard she thought about it no answers seemed to come. She decided to take a break and not think about it for a while. She went to the mall where she always enjoyed browsing in the bookstore she wasn't even thinking about the problem, the answer just popped into her head she was so excited about solving her problem she completely forgot about the bookstore.

_____

_____

_____

_____

_____

_____

G. Read the two sentences below. Then expand each sentence by adding details to make the sentences clearer and more interesting.

The tree crashed. Everyone screamed.

_____

_____

> ■ A **noun** is a word that names a person, place, thing, or quality.
>   EXAMPLE: **Nan Ford** is my **friend.**

■ **Circle the nouns in each sentence.**

1. Lupe Garcia has worked here for years and is now a supervisor.

2. The triangular piece of land at the mouth of a river is called a delta.

3. Gilbert Stuart, an American artist, painted the portraits of five American presidents.

4. Albert Einstein, the greatest scientist of our century, was born in Germany.

5. The greatest library of the ancient world was in Alexandria, Egypt.

6. Jim Thorpe, born in Oklahoma, is ranked among America's greatest athletes.

7. Mahalia Jackson was noted as a singer of spirituals.

8. Marconi invented the wireless telegraph.

9. Do you watch the parades and football games on television on New Year's Day?

10. Pocahontas, daughter of Powhatan, saved the life of Captain John Smith.

11. The *Boston News-Letter* was the first newspaper in the United States.

12. The first wireless message was sent across the English Channel in the nineteenth century.

13. Chicago is a city on Lake Michigan.

14. His seat is by the window.

15. Jack likes his new school.

16. They have promised the children a trip to Carlsbad Caverns.

17. Washington, D.C., is the capital of the United States.

18. Thomas Jefferson wrote most of our Declaration of Independence.

19. Maria was excited about her new car.

20. Hailstones are frozen raindrops, but snowflakes are not.

21. The days are usually warm in the summer.

22. Many of our rivers were named by explorers.

23. Jeff built a carport to store his boat.

24. California is home to many movie stars.

25. William Caxton printed the first book in England.

26. Chris bought tomatoes, lettuce, and cherries at the market.

27. That building has offices, stores, and apartments.

28. Marcy drove to Peoria to see her grandmother.

29. The airport was closed for five hours due to a snowstorm.

30. My pen is almost out of ink.

Common and Proper Nouns

- There are two main classes of nouns: **common nouns** and **proper nouns.**
- A **common noun** names any one of a class of objects.
  EXAMPLES: child, tree, home
- A **proper noun** names a particular person, place, or thing. It begins with a capital letter.
  EXAMPLES: Andrew Jackson, Chicago, Statue of Liberty

A. Circle the common nouns, and underline the proper nouns in each sentence.

1. In the story, a prince and a pauper changed clothing.

2. New York and Los Angeles are the largest cities in the United States.

3. Do you remember the story about Scrooge and Tiny Tim?

4. Sumatra is a large island in the Indian Ocean.

5. In the United States, hail causes more damage than tornadoes do.

6. We learned to make paper from the Chinese.

7. "Rikki-tikki-tavi," by Rudyard Kipling, is a story about a mongoose.

8. *Shamrock* is the name commonly given to the national emblem of Ireland.

9. The shilling is a silver coin used in England.

10. The lights of our car were reflected in the wet pavement.

11. Nathan, did you come with Sammy last Tuesday?

12. The Great Sphinx is the most famous monument in Egypt.

13. My family visited Mexico and Canada this year.

B. Write a common noun suggested by each proper noun.

1. Panama _____

2. *Treasure Island* _____

3. Linda _____

4. Kansas _____

5. Beethoven _____

6. Pacific _____

7. Iceland _____

8. Saturn _____

9. Mrs. Taylor _____

10. Africa _____

11. Edison _____

12. North America _____

13. December _____

14. Kansas City _____

15. University of Texas _____

16. Rockies _____

17. Dr. Dean _____

18. Huron _____

19. Tuesday _____

20. Thanksgiving _____

C. Write a proper noun suggested by each common noun.

1. continent _____
2. mountain _____
3. hotel _____
4. hero _____
5. inventor _____
6. building _____
7. day _____
8. physician _____
9. holiday _____
10. state _____

11. actor _____
12. magazine _____
13. month _____
14. lake _____
15. school _____
16. river _____
17. song _____
18. president _____
19. explorer _____
20. basketball team _____

D. Write a sentence in which you use a proper noun suggested to you by each phrase.

1. Your state _____

_____

2. Name of a foreign country _____

_____

3. Name of a singer _____

_____

4. Name of the make of an automobile _____

_____

5. Name of a store near your home _____

_____

6. Name of a television star _____

_____

7. Name of an ocean _____

_____

8. Name of the President of the United States _____

_____

The following chart shows how to change **singular nouns** into **plural nouns**.		
Noun	**Plural Form**	**Examples**
Most nouns	Add -s	ship, ships nose, noses
Nouns ending in a consonant and -y	Change the -y to -i, and add -es	sky, skies navy, navies
Nouns ending in -o	Add -s or -es	hero, heroes piano, pianos
Most nouns ending in -f or -fe	Change the -f or -fe to -ves	half, halves
Most nouns ending in -ch, -sh, -s, or -x	Add -es	bench, benches bush, bushes tax, taxes
Many two-word or three-word compound nouns	Add -s to the principle word	son-in-law, sons-in-law
Nouns with the same form in the singular and plural	No change	sheep

A. Fill in the blank with the plural form of the word in parentheses.

1. (brush)   These are plastic _____.

2. (lunch)   That cafe on the corner serves well-balanced _____.

3. (country)   What _____ belong to the United Nations?

4. (bench)   There are many iron _____ in the park.

5. (earring)   These _____ came from Italy.

6. (county)   How many _____ are in that state?

7. (piano)   There are three _____ in the warehouse.

8. (fox)   Did you see the _____ at the zoo?

9. (daisy)   We bought Mom a bunch of _____.

10. (potato)   Do you like baked _____?

11. (dish)   Please help wash the _____.

12. (store)   There are three _____ near my house.

B. Write the correct plural form for each singular noun.

1. booklet _____
2. tomato _____
3. truck _____
4. chef _____
5. branch _____
6. toddler _____
7. penny _____
8. potato _____
9. piece _____
10. door _____
11. island _____
12. lady _____
13. house _____
14. garage _____
15. fish _____

16. watch _____
17. elf _____
18. desk _____
19. pan _____
20. sheep _____
21. garden _____
22. pony _____
23. solo _____
24. tree _____
25. light _____
26. church _____
27. city _____
28. spoonful _____
29. vacation _____
30. home _____

C. Rewrite the sentences, changing each underlined singular noun to a plural noun.

1. Put the apple and orange in the box.

_____

2. Jan wrote five letter to her friend.

_____

3. Those building each have four elevator.

_____

4. Our family drove many mile to get to the lake.

_____

5. The top of those car were damaged in the storm.

_____

6. My aunt and uncle attended the family reunion.

_____

Possessive Nouns

30

- A **possessive noun** shows possession of the noun that follows.
- Form the possessive of most singular nouns by adding an apostrophe
  (') and -s.   EXAMPLES: a child's toy, my teacher's classroom
- Form the possessive of plural nouns ending in -s by adding only an
  apostrophe.   EXAMPLES: our books' pages, those stores' windows
- Form the possessive of plural nouns that do not end in -s by adding an
  apostrophe and -s.   EXAMPLES: some women's clothes, many men's shoes

A. Write the possessive form of each noun.

1. brother _____

2. boy _____

3. Carol _____

4. children _____

5. grandmother _____

6. lady _____

7. heroes _____

8. women _____

9. ox _____

10. ladies _____

11. Dr. Kahn _____

12. soldier _____

13. pony _____

14. friend _____

15. child _____

16. engineers _____

17. birds _____

18. girls _____

B. Write ten sentences using possessive nouns formed in Exercise A.

1. _____

2. _____

3. _____

4. _____

5. _____

6. _____

7. _____

8. _____

9. _____

10. _____

C. Complete each sentence with the possessive form of the word in parentheses.

1. (doctor) My _____ office is closed.

2. (senator) The _____ speech was astounding.

3. (sheep) What is the old saying about a wolf in _____ clothing?

4. (baby) Are the _____ hands cold?

5. (Ms. Wood) _____ classroom is on this floor.

6. (collectors) Let's form a _____ club.

7. (spider) A _____ web has a complicated design.

8. (Mr. Smith) _____ store was damaged by the flood.

9. (Tim) _____ brother found this purse.

10. (Aunt Beth) _____ business is successful.

11. (Carl Sandburg) _____ poems are enjoyed by people of all ages.

12. (child) The _____ book is torn.

13. (ladies) That store sells _____ hats.

14. (elephants) There were seats on the _____ backs.

15. (sister) My _____ room is at the front of the house.

16. (America) What is the name of _____ largest river?

17. (friends) Those are my _____ homes.

18. (bird) That _____ nest is very close to the ground.

19. (children) The library has a table of _____ books.

20. (owl) I heard an _____ hoot during the night.

21. (brothers) Please get your _____ shirts from the drier.

22. (student) The _____ pen ran out of ink.

23. (country) We sang our _____ national anthem.

24. (owner) The dog lay at its _____ feet.

25. (uncle) I visited my _____ laundry.

26. (Mother) _____ paintings sell well.

27. (boys) The _____ jackets are brown.

> - An **appositive** is a noun that identifies or explains the noun or pronoun it follows.
>   EXAMPLE: My dog, **Fido,** won a medal.
> - An **appositive phrase** consists of an appositive and its modifiers.
>   EXAMPLE: My book, **a novel about the Civil War,** is one of the best I've read.
> - Use **commas** to set off an appositive or an appositive phrase that is not essential to the meaning of the sentence.
>   EXAMPLE: John Gray, my uncle, owns that home.
> - Don't use commas if the appositive is essential to the meaning of the sentence.
>   EXAMPLES: My brother Kevin arrived late. My other brother Charlie arrived early.

A. Underline the appositive or appositive phrase, and circle the noun that it identifies.

1. Tom, a member of our class, decided to run a clean-up campaign.

2. Our teacher, Mrs. Tobins, thought it was a wonderful idea.

3. My friend Andy wanted to help.

4. Mary, the best organizer in the class, suggested that we form committees.

5. The clean-up committee, the largest group, would pick up the trash.

6. My committee, the garbage removal group, would bag and throw away what the others picked up.

7. Marcia, the head of the cafeteria committee, told everyone to bring brooms.

8. Her friend Theresa brought a broom and a rake.

9. The most popular committee, the paint committee, needed brushes and ladders.

10. Our school, Thomas Jefferson, looked great when we were finished.

B. Complete each sentence with an appropriate appositive.

1. My classmate _____ bought a new bike.

2. The bike, _____, is fast and sleek.

3. Joe and his friend _____ plan to race their bikes.

4. They will race to Pease Park, _____, on Tuesday.

5. They plan to meet Anne, _____, on the bike path.

6. After bicycling, they will see a movie, _____.

7. Our friend _____ might come with us.

8. We will get a snack, _____, to eat during the movie.

9. My favorite actor, _____, might be in the movie.

Action Verbs

> - A **verb** is a word that expresses action, being, or state of being.
>   EXAMPLE: Paul **went** to school.
> - An **action verb** is a verb that expresses action.
>   EXAMPLE: The track star **ran** fast.

- **Underline the action verb in each sentence.**

    1. Watch your favorite television program.

    2. Andrea carefully dusted her new piano.

    3. Anna, copy the exercise carefully.

    4. A wood fire burned in the huge fireplace.

    5. This button fell from my grandmother's sweater.

    6. The Harlem Globe Trotters play basketball throughout the world.

    7. The musicians practiced for the concert.

    8. The waves dashed the light craft against the rocks.

    9. A sentence expresses a complete thought.

    10. Everybody enjoys a good laugh.

    11. This long, narrow trail leads to the mountaintop.

    12. It snowed almost every day in February.

    13. We hiked through the southern part of Arizona.

    14. Dan made me a delicious sandwich.

    15. Please hand me the salt, Beth.

    16. Draw a line under each verb.

    17. We skated on Lake Superior.

    18. The little girl answered all my questions.

    19. The city repaired that pothole last week.

    20. The early settlers suffered many hardships.

    21. Write your sentence on the board.

    22. They moved the car from the street.

    23. Thomas Edison often worked eighteen hours a day.

    24. Carol directs the community choir.

    25. The team played softball all afternoon.

    26. We walked along the beach for an hour.

    27. Who helped you with your science project?

    28. The bridge collapsed.

    29. The antique clock ticked loudly.

Linking Verbs

- A **linking verb** does not show action. Instead, it links the subject to a word that either describes the subject or gives the subject another name.
- A verb is a linking verb if it can replace one of the verbs of being (<u>am</u>, <u>is</u>, <u>are</u>, <u>was</u>, <u>were</u>).
  EXAMPLES: We **were** cold. Nancy **is** a dancer. John **looked** tired.
  The soup **tastes** delicious.

A. Underline the linking verb in each sentence.

1. Carla appears nervous.

2. She is the first singer on the program.

3. Last year, she was last on the program.

4. Another performer is last this year.

5. The stage looks beautiful.

6. Flowers are everywhere.

7. The flowers smell fresh.

8. Carla feels ready to start.

9. Her song sounds wonderful.

10. The audience seems pleased.

B. Complete each sentence with a linking verb from the box. You may use any verb more than once.

am	appeared	are	became	is	seemed	was	were

1. Tony _____ frightened.

2. He _____ alone in the cabin for the first time.

3. In the dark forest, everything _____ threatening.

4. Because of the storm, the lights _____ out.

5. Even the shadows _____ strange.

6. "This _____ stupid," he thought to himself.

7. "I _____ brave; I'm not a coward."

8. "Where _____ Father?" he wondered.

9. There _____ bears in the woods.

10. What if he _____ lost?

Principal Parts of Verbs

> - A verb has four principal parts: **present, present participle, past,** and **past participle.**
> - For regular verbs, form the present participle by adding -ing to the present. Use a form of the helping verb be with the present participle.
> - Form the past and past participle by adding -ed to the present. Use a form of the helping verb have with the past participle.
>
>   EXAMPLES:
>
> | Present | Present Participle | Past | Past Participle |
> |---------|--------------------|------|-----------------|
> | laugh | (is) laughing | laughed | (have, has, had) laughed |
> | bake | (is) baking | baked | (have, has, had) baked |
> | live | (is) living | lived | (have, has, had) lived |
>
> - Irregular verbs form their past and past participle in other ways. A dictionary shows the principal parts of these verbs.

- Write the present participle, past, and past participle for each verb.

PRESENT	PRESENT PARTICIPLE	PAST	PAST PARTICIPLE
1. stop	is stopping	stopped	(have, has, had) stopped
2. listen			
3. carry			
4. help			
5. start			
6. borrow			
7. call			
8. receive			
9. hope			
10. illustrate			
11. divide			
12. change			
13. score			
14. iron			
15. study			
16. collect			
17. laugh			

> ■ A **verb phrase** consists of a main verb and one or more **helping verbs.** A helping verb is also called an **auxiliary verb.** In a verb phrase, the helping verb or verbs precede the main verb.   EXAMPLE: James **has arrived.**
> ■ The helping verbs are:
>   am, are, is, was, were, be, being, been
>   has, have, had
>   do, does, did
>   can, could, must, may, might, shall, should, will, would

A. Write a sentence using each word below as the main verb in a verb phrase.

1. gone _____

2. written _____

3. come _____

4. thrown _____

5. draw _____

6. walking _____

7. invent _____

8. sing _____

9. seen _____

10. eaten _____

B. Underline the verb phrase in each sentence.

1. My sister Carolyn has returned from a vacation in Florida.

2. She has planned to tell us all about it.

3. Carolyn would have answered every question about her trip.

4. Our club officers have been looking for someone to speak.

5. The officers have asked Carolyn to the meeting.

6. They have organized an interesting meeting.

7. Every detail of the meeting has been planned carefully.

8. I must speak to Carolyn immediately.

9. The lights were dimmed for Carolyn's slide show.

10. She said that alligators had been seen in some places.

11. Pets and farm animals were threatened by them.

12. We are planning a trip to Florida next year.

Verb Tenses

> - The **tense** of a verb tells the time of the action or being. There are three simple tenses—present, past, and future.
> - **Present tense** tells about what is happening now.
>   EXAMPLES: Conrad **is** busy. Conrad **studies** hard.
> - **Past tense** tells about something that happened before.
>   EXAMPLE: Conrad **was** sick yesterday.
> - **Future tense** tells about something that will happen. The auxiliary verbs will and shall are used in future tense.
>   EXAMPLES: Conrad **will take** the test tomorrow. I **shall keep** my word.

A. Complete each sentence by writing a verb in the tense shown in parentheses.

1. (future) Hilary _____ tomorrow.

2. (future) Joe _____ her up at the airport.

3. (past) We _____ the house yesterday.

4. (past) Carl _____ reservations for tomorrow night.

5. (present) Hilary _____ my best friend.

6. (future) We _____ on a sightseeing tour.

7. (present) I _____ very excited about Hilary's visit.

8. (past) Margaret _____ Aunt Toby last week.

B. Write present, past, or future for the tense of each underlined verb.

1. School will end next month. _____

2. We studied hard yesterday. _____

3. Final exams will start soon. _____

4. I review every evening. _____

5. This method worked at midterm. _____

6. I got A's on my tests then. _____

7. Marty studies with me. _____

8. We will study every evening this week. _____

9. I hardly studied last year. _____

10. My grades showed it, too. _____

Present Perfect and Past Perfect Tenses

- The **perfect tenses** express action that happened before another time or event.
- The **present perfect** tense tells about something that happened at an indefinite time in the past. The present perfect tense consists of <u>has</u> or <u>have</u> + the past participle.
   EXAMPLES: I **have eaten** already. He **has eaten,** too.
- The **past perfect** tense tells about something that happened before something else in the past. The past perfect tense consists of <u>had</u> + the past participle.
   EXAMPLE: I already **had eaten** when they arrived.

A. Write <u>present perfect</u> and <u>past perfect</u> for the tense of the underlined verbs.

_____ 1. Jan <u>had completed</u> seventh grade in June.

_____ 2. She <u>had gone</u> to school in Memphis before coming here.

_____ 3. Jan <u>has decided</u> that she likes her new school.

_____ 4. She <u>had been worried</u> that she wouldn't fit in.

_____ 5. Jan <u>has lived</u> in her house for eight months.

_____ 6. We <u>have tried</u> to make Jan feel welcome.

_____ 7. She <u>has told</u> us a lot about Memphis.

_____ 8. We <u>had known</u> Memphis was an important city.

_____ 9. However, Jan <u>has described</u> things we never knew!

_____ 10. We <u>have decided</u> that we would like to visit Tennessee some day.

B. Complete each sentence with <u>have</u>, <u>has</u>, or <u>had</u> to form the verb tense indicated in parentheses.

1. (present perfect) The pitcher _____ left the mound.

2. (present perfect) The coach and catcher _____ talked to him.

3. (past perfect) The coach _____ warned him to be careful.

4. (present perfect) Jason _____ taken his place on the mound.

5. (past perfect) Jason _____ pitched ten games by the end of last season.

6. (present perfect) Jason _____ pitched very well.

7. (past perfect) The team _____ won every game last week.

Unit 3, Grammar and Usage

> - Use <u>is</u> and <u>was</u> with a singular subject.   EXAMPLE: Here **is** Roberto.
> - Use <u>are</u> and <u>were</u> with a plural subject.   EXAMPLE: There **are** Dr. Thomas and <u>Dr</u>. Williams.
> - Always use <u>are</u> and <u>were</u> with the pronoun <u>you</u>.   EXAMPLES: You **are** my favorite cousin. You **are** late today.

■ **Circle the verb that agrees with the subject of each sentence.**

1. Here (is, are) the box of paper clips you ordered.

2. There (is, are) three girls named Laura in our apartment building.

3. There (is, are) a small chance of showers tomorrow.

4. Senator Thompson (is, are) going to speak today.

5. Here (is, are) the tools you asked me to bring.

6. There (is, are) much to be done.

7. Two of these chairs (is, are) damaged.

8. (Is, Are) these cars really being offered for sale?

9. Kelly, (is, are) this your car?

10. Many people (is, are) planning to go to the hockey game.

11. Juan and I (was, were) afraid that Carlos (was, were) not going to arrive on time.

12. Who (was, were) you talking to this afternoon?

13. A group of truck drivers (was, were) in the cafe.

14. There (was, were) many kinds of rare plants in the garden.

15. Several visitors (was, were) here this afternoon.

16. Anita, (wasn't, weren't) you interested in working overtime?

17. Why (wasn't, weren't) these dishes washed last night?

18. The mistakes in punctuation (was, were) carefully checked.

19. Ricardo and Sara (wasn't, weren't) able to help us.

20. There (was, were) two large trays of sandwiches on the picnic table.

21. Each picture for the exhibit (was, were) carefully selected.

22. One of the sisters (was, were) enrolled at a university.

23. Each of the letters (was, were) read aloud.

24. (Was, Were) you planning to go to the park today?

25. Did you know that there (was, were) two new families in our apartment building?

26. (Wasn't, Weren't) you at the annual meeting, Ben?

27. Three of the people (was, were) injured when the accident occurred.

28. (Was, Were) your aunt and uncle the first to build a house on this block?

29. Who (was, were) the first settlers in your community?

Past Tenses of *Give, Take,* and *Write*

- Never use a helping verb with gave, took, and wrote.
- Always use a helping verb with given, taken, and written.

A. Underline the correct verb.

1. It (took, taken) the mechanic only a few minutes to change the tire.

2. Has anyone (took, taken) my note pad?

3. Who (wrote, written) the best letter?

4. I have (wrote, written) a thank-you note.

5. Tell me who (gave, given) you that address.

6. Have you (gave, given) the dog its food?

7. Bill hadn't (wrote, written) this poem.

8. Have you finally (wrote, written) for the tickets?

9. Sam had (gave, given) the lecture on boat safety yesterday at the Y.M.C.A.

10. Alicia and I (wrote, written) a letter to the editor.

11. Haven't you (took, taken) your seat yet?

12. We had our picture (took, taken) yesterday.

13. Who (gave, given) you these old magazines?

14. The workers (took, taken) all their equipment with them.

15. A friend had (gave, given) us the furniture.

16. Leslie had (wrote, written) the letter over three weeks ago.

17. Who (took, taken) the most photographs on the trip?

18. The doctor (gave, given) me a tetanus shot after I cut my hand.

19. Has Henry (wrote, written) to Aunt Julia yet?

B. Write the correct past tense form of each verb in parentheses to complete the sentences.

1. (take) Frances recently _____ her dog, Ralph, to the veterinarian.

2. (write) The doctor had _____ to say that Ralph needed his annual shots.

3. (give) An assistant _____ Ralph a dog biscuit as soon as he arrived.

4. (give) That way Ralph was _____ something that would distract him.

5. (take) Before Ralph knew it, the doctor had _____ a sample of his blood.

6. (take) It only _____ a minute to give Ralph his shots.

7. (give) The doctor _____ Ralph a pat on the head.

8. (take) "You have _____ very good care of Ralph," he said.

Past Tenses of *See, Go,* and *Begin*

> - Never use a helping verb with <u>saw</u>, <u>went</u>, and <u>began</u>.
> - Always use a helping verb with <u>seen</u>, <u>gone</u>, and <u>begun</u>.

A. Underline the correct verb.

1. The last person we (saw, seen) in the park was Eric.

2. Who has (went, gone) for the ice?

3. Carla and Yoko (began, begun) to fix the flat tire.

4. Charles (went, gone) to the supermarket for some lettuce.

5. Our summer vacation has (began, begun).

6. They had (saw, seen) a shooting star.

7. Hasn't she (went, gone) to the airport?

8. Yes, we (saw, seen) the concert poster.

9. Alice, have you ever (saw, seen) a penguin?

10. We never (went, gone) to hear the new mayor speak.

11. Olivia, why haven't you (began, begun) your work?

12. Mike (began, begun) to tell us about the accident.

13. Our guests have (went, gone).

14. It (began, begun) to snow early in the evening.

15. Work has finally (began, begun) on the new stadium.

16. We (saw, seen) Pikes Peak last summer.

17. My three sisters (went, gone) to Wichita, Kansas.

18. Have you (saw, seen) the waves pounding the huge boulders?

19. We (went, gone) to hear the symphony last night.

20. They (began, begun) their program with music by Mozart.

21. The program (began, begun) on time.

B. Write a sentence using each verb below.

1. saw _____

2. seen _____

3. gone _____

4. went _____

5. began _____

6. begun _____

> - Never use a helping verb with <u>wore</u>, <u>rose</u>, <u>stole</u>, <u>chose</u>, and <u>broke</u>.
> - Always use a helping verb with <u>worn</u>, <u>risen</u>, <u>stolen</u>, <u>chosen</u>, and <u>broken</u>.

A. Underline the correct verb.

1. We almost froze because we hadn't (wore, worn) coats.

2. Haven't you (chose, chosen) a new shirt?

3. We (broke, broken) the new bike.

4. The river (rose, risen) two feet during the night.

5. Someone had (stole, stolen) our car last week.

6. Mrs. White had (chose, chosen) many of our old landmarks for the city tour.

7. I have (wore, worn) these uncomfortable shoes for the last time.

8. We were miles along the way when the sun (rose, risen).

9. The squirrels have (stole, stolen) most of our acorns.

10. The airplane (rose, risen) above the clouds.

11. The children have (wore, worn) a path through the backyard.

12. They (chose, chosen) to stay at the camp for a day.

13. Jan had (broke, broken) her leg the summer we visited her.

14. Have you ever (stole, stolen) home base?

15. Our pizza dough had (rose, risen) by the time we sliced the pepperoni.

16. The bottle's protective seal was (broke, broken), so we returned it to the store.

17. Kurt and Jamie (wore, worn) each other's clothes when they were younger.

18. The full moon had (rose, risen) over the deep, dark lake.

19. The jewel thief (stole, stolen) one too many diamonds before he got caught.

B. Circle any mistakes in the use of past tense verbs.

The sun had just rose when Kate recognized the familiar sound of fishing boats returning to shore. She hadn't meant to sleep late this morning, but the early morning waves had coaxed her back to sleep. Now, slipping into her sweatshirt, thongs, and damp shorts, Kate noticed that seagulls had again stole fish from the pail of bait. She chuckled at the thought, and then tossed the circling birds another minnow. Turning, Kate noticed Luke nearing the boat. He worn the same windbreaker and soft, leather shoes nearly every day since they first met, months ago. Kate paused for a moment. It occurred to her that she chosen a good friend. Luke had never broke a shoestring, or a promise.

> - Never use a helping verb with <u>came</u>, <u>rang</u>, <u>drank</u>, <u>knew</u>, and <u>threw</u>.
> - Always use a helping veb with <u>come</u>, <u>rung</u>, <u>drunk</u>, <u>known</u>, and <u>thrown</u>.

A. Underline the correct verb.

1. The tired horse (drank, drunk) from the cool stream.

2. The church bell has not (rang, rung) today.

3. I haven't (drank, drunk) my hot chocolate.

4. We (knew, known) that it was time to go.

5. Have you (threw, thrown) the garbage out?

6. Haven't the movers (came, come) for our furniture?

7. We (rang, rung) the fire alarm five minutes ago.

8. Haven't you (know, known) him for a long time?

9. I (threw, thrown) the ball to James.

10. My cousins from Springfield, Missouri, (came, come) this afternoon.

11. Why haven't you (drank, drunk) your milk?

12. I always (came, come) to work in my wheelchair now.

13. I (knew, known) Patty when she was just a little girl.

14. Have you (threw, thrown) away last week's newspaper?

15. We have (came, come) to tell you something.

16. If you already (rang, rung) the bell, then you might try knocking.

17. Tony thinks he (drank, drunk) something that made him ill.

B. Write a sentence using each verb below.

1. came _____

2. come _____

3. rang _____

4. rung _____

5. threw _____

6. thrown _____

7. drank _____

8. drunk _____

9. knew _____

- Never use a helping verb with <u>ate</u>, <u>fell</u>, <u>drew</u>, <u>drove</u>, and <u>ran</u>.
- Always use a helping verb with <u>eaten</u>, <u>fallen</u>, <u>drawn</u>, <u>driven</u>, and <u>run</u>.

A. Underline the correct verb.

1. Ed, have you (drew, drawn) your diagram?

2. When we had (drove, driven) for two hours, we (began, begun) to feel hungry.

3. All of our pears have (fell, fallen) from the tree.

4. After we had (ate, eaten) our dinner, we (ran, run) around the lake.

5. A great architect (drew, drawn) the plans for our civic center.

6. We had just (ran, run) into the house when we saw our friends.

7. Hadn't the building already (fell, fallen) when you (ran, run) around the corner?

8. Those heavy curtains in the theater have (fell, fallen) down.

9. Last week we (drove, driven) to the lake for a vacation.

10. I have just (ate, eaten) a delicious slice of watermelon.

11. I (ate, eaten) my breakfast before six o'clock this morning.

12. All of the leaves have (fell, fallen) from the elm trees.

13. When was the last time you (ran, run) a mile?

B. Write the correct past tense form of each verb in parentheses to complete the sentences.

1. (drive)   Last weekend we _____ to the lake for a picnic.

2. (draw)   Since Jenna knew several shortcuts, she _____ a detailed map for us.

3. (fall)   She mentioned that during a recent summer storm, debris had _____ on many of the roads.

4. (fall)   She warned us that a large tree _____ on one of the main roads.

5. (drive)   Jenna claimed that she had never _____ under such dangerous circumstances.

6. (run)   "I almost _____ right into that tree in the dark!" Jenna said.

7. (eat)   In order to avoid traveling at night, we _____ our dinner after we got home from the lake.

8. (eat)   We had _____ so much during our picnic that none of us minded waiting!

9. (draw)   Once home, we all agreed that Jenna had _____ a great map for us.

10. (run)   We made the trip in record time, and we hadn't _____ over any trees in the process!

> - Never use a helping verb with <u>did</u>.
>   EXAMPLE: Anne **did** a great job on her test.
> - Always use a helping verb with <u>done</u>.
>   EXAMPLE: Hallie **had** also **done** a great job.
> - <u>Doesn't</u> is the contraction of <u>does not</u>. Use it with singular nouns and the pronouns <u>he</u>, <u>she</u>, and <u>it</u>.
>   EXAMPLES: Rachel **doesn't** want to go. It **doesn't** seem right.
> - <u>Don't</u> is the contraction of <u>do not</u>. Use it with plural nouns and with the pronouns <u>I</u>, <u>you</u>, <u>we</u>, and <u>they</u>.
>   EXAMPLES: Mr. and Mrs. Ricci **don't** live there. You **don't** have your purse.

A. Underline the correct verb.

1. Why (doesn't, don't) Lois have the car keys?

2. Show me the way you (did, done) it.

3. Have the three of you (did, done) most of the work?

4. Why (doesn't, don't) she cash a check today?

5. Please show me what damage the storm (did, done).

6. (Doesn't, Don't) the workers on the morning shift do a fine job?

7. Have the new owners of our building (did, done) anything about the plumbing?

8. (Doesn't, Don't) those apples look overly ripe?

9. Chris (doesn't, don't) want to do the spring cleaning this week.

10. The gloves and the hat (doesn't, don't) match.

11. Carolyn, have you (did, done) your homework today?

12. Who (did, done) this fine job of painting?

13. (Doesn't, Don't) the tile in our new kitchen look nice?

14. (Doesn't, Don't) that dog stay in a fenced yard?

15. He has (did, done) me a great favor.

16. I will help if he (doesn't, don't).

B. Write one sentence using <u>did</u> and one sentence using <u>done</u>.

1. _____

2. _____

C. Write one sentence using <u>doesn't</u> and one sentence using <u>don't</u>.

1. _____

2. _____

Transitive and Intransitive Verbs

- There are two kinds of action verbs: **transitive** and **intransitive.**
- A transitive verb has a direct object.

                                  D.O.

      EXAMPLE: Father **painted** the house.

- An intransitive verb does not need an object to complete its meaning.

      EXAMPLES: The sun **rises** in the east. She **walks** quickly.

A. Underline the verb in each sentence. Then write <u>T</u> for transitive or <u>I</u> for intransitive.

_____ **1.** Kristina joined the swim team in March.

_____ **2.** She wanted the exercise.

_____ **3.** Kristina swam every day after school.

_____ **4.** Her coach worked with her each practice.

_____ **5.** She learned the backstroke.

_____ **6.** One of her teammates helped.

_____ **7.** Kristina practiced for hours.

_____ **8.** Once, she won a race.

_____ **9.** She yelled excitedly.

_____ **10.** The coach gave her the ribbon.

_____ **11.** Kristina's family congratulated her.

_____ **12.** They had enjoyed watching her swim.

_____ **13.** Kristina hoped that she would win again.

_____ **14.** Soon she was helping other swimmers, as well.

B. Underline the transitive verb, and circle the direct object in each sentence.

1. Carlos walked Tiny every day.

2. Tiny usually pulled Carlos along.

3. Carlos washed Tiny every other week.

4. Tiny loved water.

5. He splashed Carlos whenever he could.

6. Tiny also loved rawhide bones.

7. He chewed the bones until they were gone.

8. Carlos found Tiny when Tiny was just a puppy.

- A **verbal** is a verb form that functions as a noun or adjective. There are three types of verbals: **infinitives, participles,** and **gerunds.**
- An **infinitive** is the base form of the verb, commonly preceded by <u>to</u>. An infinitive that functions as a noun is a verbal.
  EXAMPLE: The object of the game is **to win.**
- A present or past **participle** that functions as an adjective is a verbal.
  EXAMPLES: A **running** horse galloped down the road. **Dried** leaves flew from his hooves.
- A **gerund** is the present participle of a verb form ending in <u>-ing</u> that is used as a noun.
  EXAMPLE: **Skiing** is her favorite sport.

A. Underline the infinitive in each sentence below.

1. Al refused to quit.

2. The only thing he wanted was to finish.

3. Al had trained to run this race for months.

4. It was not important to win.

5. Al simply needed to finish.

6. He hoped to accomplish his goal.

7. Soon he was close enough to see the finish line.

B. Underline the participle in each sentence below.

1. A yelling cheerleader led the crowd.

2. The excited crowd roared.

3. The running team took the field.

4. The marching band started to play.

5. Chosen members of the band flashed cards.

6. The flashing cards spelled a message.

7. The interested students studied hard.

C. Underline the gerund in each sentence below.

1. Studying is an important job.

2. Language arts and reading help improve your language ability.

3. Learning can be rewarding.

4. Memorizing is another skill you can learn.

5. Remembering is not always easy.

6. Do you think studying is time well spent?

7. Dancing is Lauren's favorite activity.

D. Underline the verbal in each sentence, and write infinitive, participle, or gerund on the line.

_____	1. To act in a play is an honor.
_____	2. Acting can be very exciting.
_____	3. To write plays takes a lot of skill.
_____	4. Working in the theater is interesting.
_____	5. Sally wanted to participate.
_____	6. The hurried director got ready for the auditions.
_____	7. Sally prepared a moving scene.
_____	8. She was finally ready to read her scene.
_____	9. Auditioning can scare anyone.
_____	10. Sally's stirring performance won her a part.
_____	11. Rehearsing can take up much time.
_____	12. The actors must work long hours to memorize their parts.
_____	13. Sally's convincing performance was outstanding.
_____	14. All of the actors excelled in performing.
_____	15. The smiling director congratulated the cast.
_____	16. "To act is an art," said the director.
_____	17. He called them all budding artists.
_____	18. Performing is a pleasure for Yolanda.
_____	19. Bowing is even more fun.
_____	20. The audience could tell by Yolanda's face that she enjoyed playing the part.
_____	21. To continue her studies is her goal.
_____	22. Stretching is very important to athletes.
_____	23. Cramped muscles cause problems.
_____	24. You should always stretch before running.
_____	25. Loose muscles are needed to run.
_____	26. Stretched muscles work better.

Active and Passive Voice

> - **Voice** refers to the relation of a subject to its verb.
> - In the **active voice,** the subject acts.
>   EXAMPLE: **I painted** the house.
> - In the **passive voice,** the subject receives the action.
>   EXAMPLE: The house **was painted** by me.
> - Only transitive verbs are used in the passive voice.

A. Write A if the sentence is in the active voice and P if it is in the passive voice.

_____ 1. Marty applied for a summer job in a grocery store.

_____ 2. He needs money for gas and car repairs.

_____ 3. He will handle the cash register.

_____ 4. Marty will also stock the shelves.

_____ 5. The application was turned in last week.

_____ 6. The store's manager reads every application.

_____ 7. Then the applicants are interviewed.

_____ 8. Marty was interviewed on Monday.

_____ 9. The manager was impressed by Marty.

_____ 10. He will give Marty the job.

B. Rewrite each sentence in the active voice.

1. Katie was given a job babysitting by the McNeils.

   _____

2. The children will be watched by her every day.

   _____

3. Katie will be driven to their house by her father.

   _____

C. Rewrite each sentence in the passive voice.

1. Trina plays the drums in the band.

   _____

2. She chose the drums because her father played drums.

   _____

3. Trina won an award for her playing.

   _____

> - A **subject pronoun** is used in the subject of a sentence and after a linking verb.
>   EXAMPLES: **We** are going to the tournament. The woman in the suit is **she.**
> - An **object pronoun** is used after an action verb or a preposition.
>   EXAMPLE: James threw the ball to **me.**
> - A **possessive pronoun** is used to show ownership of something.
>   EXAMPLES: The red shoes are **mine.** Those are **my** red shoes.
> - An **indefinite pronoun** does not refer to a specific person or thing.
>   EXAMPLE: **Someone** should take that history class.
> - Use who as a subject pronoun, and use whom as an object pronoun.
>   EXAMPLES: **Who** is going to the party? We will ask **whom** to go with us?

A. Underline each correct pronoun.

1. Miss Matson spoke to Jennifer and (I, me) about it.

2. Uncle Stan sent Tom and (they, them) some new shirts.

3. Please bring Anne and (I, me) some cool water.

4. Here comes (my, me) brother David.

5. Susan and (he, him) were late today.

6. Was it (she, her) who answered the knock?

7. I don't believe it was (they, them)!

8. Mona took Doug and (we, us) to work.

9. He told Steven and (she, her) about the problem.

10. Don't you think (someone, us) should help?

11. Rosa and (I, me) are going to work until seven o'clock.

12. It wasn't (your, yours) cat that meowed.

13. (He, Him) and Chris are going to the game.

14. She told Katie and (my, me) parents about her fishing trip.

15. (Who, Whom) did you say got here early?

16. He said that it was (they, them) who came to our house.

17. (Everyone, We) will carry his or her own bundles.

18. It was (they, their) babysitter who knocked on the door.

19. (Who, Whom) did you meet for lunch?

20. Elizabeth and (she, her) always sit together.

21. This sweater is (hers, she).

22. (Who, Whom) led the band in the parade?

23. The red car is (our, ours).

24. Can you predict (who, whom) will win the election?

B. Underline each pronoun.

1. I told you to speak to him about our fishing trip.

2. Who is speaking?

3. They saw us when we passed by their house.

4. Just between you and me, I want to go with them.

5. He and Mike are going with us.

6. My decision to leave was made before our conversation.

7. Whom did you see?

8. This package was sent to you and me.

9. They are going with us to the game.

10. Jerry broke his arm.

11. Who told them?

12. She is my friend who moved to Chicago.

13. This check is mine.

14. Someone took some fresh flowers to them.

15. Who is she?

16. She went with us to the parade.

17. John, who is the president of that company?

18. Will she go with you?

19. Who telephoned me?

20. Should we eat with them at the picnic?

21. Which is your raincoat?

22. Did I tell you about our plans?

23. Which is mine?

24. Do you recall your cousin's middle initial?

25. Why can't you come with us?

26. Did anybody get a letter?

27. You and I are on the list, too.

28. Did you see him?

C. Write sentences using the following pronouns:

1. theirs _____

2. you and I _____

3. you and me _____

4. them _____

5. anyone _____

> - An **antecedent** is the word to which a pronoun refers.
>   EXAMPLE: **Dogs** are dangerous if **they** bite.
> - A pronoun must agree with its antecedent in **gender, (masculine, feminine,** or **neuter)** and in **number** (singular or plural).
>   EXAMPLES: **Sally** washed **her** hair. The **storm** changed **its** course.
>   The **workers** went to **their** offices.
> - If the antecedent is an indefinite pronoun (one that doesn't refer to a specific person or thing), it is correct to use a masculine pronoun. However, it is now common to use both a masculine and a feminine pronoun.
>   EXAMPLES: **Someone** lost **his** gloves. **Someone** lost **his or her** gloves.

A. Underline each pronoun. Circle its antecedent.

1. Mike said he would tutor Carmen.

2. Carmen was doing poorly in her math class.

3. Carmen often shakes her head in confusion.

4. Mike promised to try his hardest.

5. Carmen worked on her math, but it was difficult.

6. Mike and Carmen said they would work every night.

7. The math test was coming, and it promised to be hard.

8. The class was ready for its test.

9. Carmen's palms were sweaty, and they felt clammy.

10. The teacher said he knew Carmen would do well.

11. When Carmen started the test, it didn't seem so hard.

12. Each student finished his or her test and put it on the teacher's desk.

13. The teacher would correct the tests and hand them back.

14. Carmen was pleased with her grade.

B. Circle the pronoun in parentheses that agrees with the antecedent.

1. Earl and Leon practiced (their, his) free throws.

2. Each hoped practice would make (him, her) play better.

3. The team held (its, their) practice every day.

4. Leon practiced (his, their) passing.

5. It is important to study the plays because (they, he) must be remembered.

6. Carl waxed (him, his) car.

7. The building was closed because (its, their) windows were damaged in the storm.

8. The flowers opened (its, their) petals in the sunshine.

9. Maggie found (his, her) book in the closet.

10. The students piled (their, them) coats on the table.

Adjectives

> - An **adjective** is a word that modifies a noun or a pronoun.
>   EXAMPLE: He likes **chocolate** cookies.
> - Adjectives usually tell **what kind, which one,** or **how many.**
>   EXAMPLES: **bright** penny, **these** oranges, **twelve** classmates
> - A **proper adjective** is an adjective that is formed from a proper noun.
>   It always begins with a capital letter.
>   EXAMPLES: **American** continent, **English** language
> - The articles a, an, and the are called **limiting adjectives.**

A. Write three adjectives to describe each noun.

1. mountains _____   _____   _____

2. weather _____   _____   _____

3. journey _____   _____   _____

4. classroom _____   _____   _____

5. book _____   _____   _____

B. Underline each adjective.

1. This old chair is comfortable.

2. We have read a funny story recently.

3. This heavy traffic creates many dangerous situations.

4. The eager sailors collected odd souvenirs at every port.

5. The tired, thirsty soldiers marched on.

6. This is my favorite book.

7. The solitary guard walked along the lonely beach.

8. We sat in the sixth row.

9. These damp matches will not strike.

10. The children made French toast for breakfast.

11. Will you light those candles, please?

12. A red bird chirped loudly in the tall tree.

13. The heavy elephant sat down slowly.

14. A tour bus stopped at the pirate's cove.

15. The gorgeous model wore Italian leather.

16. We ate fresh seafood on our vacation.

17. Do you like mashed or baked potatoes?

18. She served Chinese food for dinner.

- A **demonstrative adjective** is one that points out a specific person or thing.
- This and that modify singular nouns. This points to a person or thing nearby, and that points to a person or thing farther away.
    - EXAMPLES: **This** movie is my favorite. **That** sign is difficult to see.
- These and those modify plural nouns. These points to persons or things nearby and those points to persons or things farther away.
    - EXAMPLES: **These** ribbons are the most colorful.
    - **Those** towels need to be folded.
- The word them is a pronoun. Never use it to describe a noun.

■ **Underline the correct demonstrative adjective.**

1. Move (those, them) plants inside since it may freeze tonight.

2. (These, That) box in front of me is too heavy to lift.

3. Who brought us (those, them) delicious cookies?

4. Look at (those, them) playful kittens.

5. (That, Those) kind of friend is appreciated.

6. (Those, Them) pictures are beautiful.

7. What are (those, them) sounds I hear?

8. Did you ever meet (those, them) people?

9. We have just developed (these, them) photographs.

10. Do you know any of (those, them) young people?

11. May we take some of (these, them) folders?

12. I have been looking over (these, them) magazines.

13. Do not eat too many of (those, them) peaches.

14. I do not like (this, these) kind of syrup.

15. (Those, Them) people should be served next.

16. Jimmy, please mail (these, them) letters.

17. Look at (those, them) posters I made!

18. (This, That) suburb is fifty miles away.

19. (These, Them) antique coins are valuable.

20. Look at (those, that) soccer players hustle!

21. Mr. Garcia, may we see (these, them) photographs?

22. Please return (that, these) library books.

23. (These, Them) clothes need to be washed.

24. Please hand me (that, those) plates.

25. (Those, Them) cookies have nuts in them.

> - An adjective has three degrees of comparison: **positive, comparative,** and **superlative.**
> - The simple form of the adjective is called the **positive** degree.
>   EXAMPLE: Ian is **short.**
> - When two people or things are being compared, the **comparative** degree is used.
>   EXAMPLE: Ian is **shorter** than Lee.
> - When three or more people or things are being compared, the **superlative** degree is used.
>   EXAMPLE: Ian is the **shortest** person in the group.
> - For all adjectives of one syllable and a few adjectives of two syllables, add -er to form the comparative degree, and -est to form the superlative degree.
>   EXAMPLE: smart—smarter—smartest
> - For some adjectives of two syllables and all adjectives of three or more syllables, use more or less to form the comparative and most or least to form the superlative.
>   EXAMPLES: This test is **more** difficult than I expected. Carol is the **most** generous of all. Katie is **less** talkative than Tom. Mary is the **least** talkative of all.

- **Complete each sentence with the correct degree of comparison of the adjective given in parentheses. Some of the forms are irregular.**

1. (changeable) The weather seems _____ this year than last.

2. (faithful) I think the dog is the _____ of all animals.

3. (agreeable) Is James _____ than Sam?

4. (busy) Theresa is the _____ person in the office.

5. (long) Which is the _____ river, the Mississippi or the Amazon?

6. (lovely) I think the rose is the _____ of all flowers.

7. (fresh) Show me the _____ cookies in the store.

8. (high) Which of the two mountains is _____?

9. (enjoyable) Which is the _____, television or the movies?

10. (reckless) That person is the _____ driver in town.

11. (young) Of all the players, Maria is the _____.

12. (tall) Alberto is the _____ of the three men.

13. (difficult) Isn't the seventh problem _____ than the eighth?

14. (quiet) We have found the _____ spot in the park.

Adverbs

- An **adverb** is a word that modifies a verb, an adjective, or another adverb.
  EXAMPLES: The rain poured **steadily**. His memories were **extremely** vivid. She responded **very** quickly.
- An adverb usually tells **how, when, where,** or **how often.**
- Many adverbs end in -ly.

A. Underline each adverb.

1. The person read slowly but clearly and expressively.

2. Adam, you are driving too recklessly.

3. The airplane started moving slowly but quickly gained speed.

4. I spoke too harshly to my friends.

5. How did all of you get here?

6. I looked everywhere for my pen.

7. The man stopped suddenly and quickly turned around.

8. Stacy read that poem too rapidly.

9. Janice plays the guitar well.

10. The little fellow was sleeping soundly.

11. The car was running noisily.

12. We returned early.

13. Those trees were severely damaged in the fire.

14. Jack ran quickly, but steadily, in the race.

B. Write two adverbs that could be used to modify each verb.

1. read _____   _____

2. think _____   _____

3. walk _____   _____

4. eat _____   _____

5. sing _____   _____

6. speak _____   _____

7. dive _____   _____

8. study _____   _____

9. write _____   _____

10. look _____   _____

Comparing With Adverbs

54

> - An **adverb** has three degrees of comparison: **positive, comparative,** and **superlative.**
> - The simple form of the adverb is called the **positive** degree.
>   EXAMPLE: Kathy ran **fast** in the race.
> - When two actions are being compared, the **comparative** degree is used.
>   EXAMPLE: Amy ran **faster** than Kathy.
> - When three or more actions are being compared, the **superlative** degree is used.
>   EXAMPLE: Maureen ran the **fastest** of all.
> - Use -er to form the comparative degree and use -est to form the superlative degree of one-syllable adverbs.
> - Use more or most with longer adverbs and with adverbs that end in -ly.
>   EXAMPLES: Louisa ran **more energetically** than Bob.
>   Ms. Baker ran the **most energetically** of all the runners.

A. Underline the adverb that best completes each sentence.

1. Mark arrived (sooner, soonest) than Greg.

2. Tony arrived the (sooner, soonest) of all.

3. They had to work very (hard, harder, hardest).

4. Tony painted (more, most) carefully than Mark.

5. Mark worked (faster, fastest) than Greg, so Mark painted the walls.

6. Lauren worked the (more, most) carefully of all.

B. Complete each sentence with the proper form of the adverb in parentheses.

1. (fast)   Ramón wanted to be the _____ runner at our school.

2. (fast)   Juan could run _____ than Ramón.

3. (seriously)   Ramón trained _____ than he had before.

4. (frequently)   Ramón is on the track _____ of all the runners.

5. (quickly)   Ramón ran the sprint _____ than he did yesterday.

6. (promptly)   Ramón arrives for practice _____ of anyone on the team.

7. (promptly)   He even arrives _____ than the coach!

8. (eagerly)   Juan does warm-up exercises _____ of all the runners.

9. (carefully)   Who concentrates _____ on his timing, Juan or Ramón?

10. (hard)   The coach congratulates Ramón on being the player who works the

_____.

67

> ■ A **preposition** is a word that shows the relationship of a noun or a pronoun to another word in the sentence.
>
>   EXAMPLES: The child ran **into** the **house**. He put his boots **under** the **table**.
>
> ■ These are some commonly used prepositions:

about	against	at	between	from	of	through	under
above	among	behind	by	in	on	to	upon
across	around	beside	for	into	over	toward	with

■ **Underline each preposition in the sentences below.**

1. Can you draw a map of your state?

2. Who is the owner of this car?

3. The pecan is a common tree in the South.

4. For whom are you waiting?

5. At the meeting, he spoke to me about your athletic ability.

6. Our company is proud of its industrious employees.

7. Her sister Cindy stood beside her.

8. A small amount of that soup is all I want.

9. We went to the house at the end of the street.

10. There were seventy-five post offices in the United States in 1790.

11. Most of the spectators stood during the last quarter of the game.

12. These shoes of mine are too tight at the heel.

13. We ate dinner at the new restaurant near the river.

14. They stood on the porch and watched for the mail carrier.

15. Anyone can succeed with hard work.

16. We walked behind that group.

17. Astronaut Sally Ride was the first woman in space.

18. A group of people on horses rode behind the band.

19. We walked to the picnic grounds during the lunch hour.

20. Ben slid down the slippery hill.

21. There is a bridge across the river in our town.

22. The ball was knocked over the fence and into the pond.

23. I see a spot of dirt under your left eye.

24. One can observe a strange world below the surface of an ocean.

25. The rocket quickly disappeared behind the clouds.

26. Much of our land is drained by the Mississippi River.

27. Please sit between us.

28. This package is for you.

> - A **phrase** is a group of closely related words used as a single part of speech but not containing a subject and predicate.
>   EXAMPLE: The writer **of this novel** is signing autographs.
> - A **prepositional phrase** is a group of words that begins with a preposition and ends with a noun or pronoun.
>   EXAMPLE: He took the train **to New York.**
> - The noun or pronoun in the prepositional phrase is called the **object of the preposition.**
>   EXAMPLE: He took the train to **New York.**

- **Put parentheses around each prepositional phrase. Then underline each preposition, and circle the object of the preposition.**

1. The airplane was flying (above the clouds).

2. We are moving to North Carolina.

3. Sandra lives on the second block.

4. An old water tower once stood on that hill.

5. The car slid on the wet pavement.

6. Sealing wax was invented in the seventeenth century.

7. Motto rings were first used by the Romans.

8. Tungsten, a metal, was discovered in 1781.

9. Roses originally came from Asia.

10. The ball rolled into the street.

11. Do you always keep the puppies in a pen?

12. The children climbed over the fence.

13. She lives in Denver.

14. Columbus made three trips to America.

15. They spread the lunch under the shade of the giant elm tree.

16. The treasure was found by a skin diver.

17. A squad of soldiers marched behind the tank.

18. Shall I row across the stream?

19. Large airplanes fly across the nation.

20. Walter looked into the sack.

21. The cat ran up the pole.

22. The Pilgrims landed at Plymouth in 1620.

23. Many tourists come to our state.

24. We spent last summer in the Adirondacks.

25. Do not stand behind a parked car.

> - A prepositional phrase can be used to describe a noun or a pronoun. Then the prepositional phrase is being used as an **adjective** to tell which one, what kind, or how many.
>   EXAMPLE: The bird **in the tree** whistled.
>   The prepositional phrase in the tree tells **which** bird.
> - A prepositional phrase can be used to describe a verb. Then the prepositional phrase is being used as an **adverb** to tell how, where, or when.
>   EXAMPLE: Charlie ate breakfast **before leaving for school.**
>   The prepositional phrase **before leaving for school** tells **when** Charlie ate breakfast.

- **Underline each prepositional phrase, and classify it as adjective or adverb.**

                                adv.
1. They went <u>to the ranch</u>.

2. The first savings bank was established in France.

3. Fall Creek Falls in Tennessee is my home.

4. Return all books to the public library.

5. My aunt lives in an old house.

6. Janice bought a sweater with red trim.

7. The birds in the zoo are magnificent.

8. Jade is found in Burma.

9. I spent the remainder of my money.

10. The magician waved a wand over the hat, and a rabbit appeared.

11. The diameter of a Sequoia tree trunk can reach ten feet.

12. The capital of New York is Albany.

13. The narrowest streets are near the docks.

14. Our family went to the movie.

15. Roald Amundsen discovered the South Pole in 1911.

16. The floor in this room is painted black.

17. The dead leaves are blowing across the yard.

18. A forest of petrified wood has been found.

19. The mole's tunnel runs across the lawn.

Conjunctions

> - A **conjunction** is a word used to join words or groups of words.
>   EXAMPLES: Yuri **and** Brant have arrived. They worked **until** the sun went down.
> - These are some commonly used conjunctions:
>
> | although | because | however | or | that | when | whereas |
> |----------|---------|---------|-----|--------|---------|---------|
> | and | but | if | since | though | whether | yet |
> | as | for | nor | than | unless | while | |
>
> - Some conjunctions are used in pairs. These include either . . . or, neither . . . nor, and not only . . . but also.

■ **Underline each conjunction in the sentences below.**

1. Do you know whether Brandon is going to the employment office?

2. Jesse, are you and Ryan going to see a movie this afternoon?

3. Aunt Linda will go to the coast when the weather turns warm.

4. Gina or Vicki will take me to practice.

5. Are you and Elizabeth going swimming this Saturday?

6. Paul will be here unless he has to work.

7. Dean or I must go to the supermarket.

8. Chicken and potatoes are my favorite foods.

9. The trainer and the animals gave a good show.

10. I was angry at Megan because she was not on time.

11. Tom gets into trouble, but he usually gets out of it.

12. Carelessness is the cause of many falls and burns.

13. She stopped work because she had to leave early.

14. Matt has been understanding since I started working two jobs.

15. This chair is small, but it is comfortable.

16. Although it looked like rain, we went for a drive.

17. Kerry is two years older than Tom.

18. The remark was neither just nor kind.

19. You may go either by bus or by plane.

20. Mr. Lopez is here, but he is too busy to help us right now.

21. Let's go inside, for it is getting dark.

22. We listened closely while the directions were given.

23. Fruit is not only delicious, but also healthful.

24. Bring either a short poem or a rhyme to class tomorrow.

25. Anne neither asked for help nor received any.

26. Neither Joe nor Marie went to the show.

A. **Write the part of speech above each underlined word. Use the abbreviations given in the box.**

1. A heavy dust storm rolled across the prairie.

2. This is a nice surprise!

3. The dark clouds slowly gathered in the north.

4. Marlee and I are showing slides of the photographs that we took on our trip.

5. Is the capital of your state built on a river?

6. These shrubs are beautiful.

7. Someone opened the door very cautiously.

8. Please handle this extremely fragile china very carefully.

9. The weary people waited for the long parade to start.

10. Large herds of longhorn cattle grazed on these vast plains.

11. We are going to the new mall today.

12. Floyd, you are eating that food too rapidly.

n.	noun
pron.	pronoun
v.	verb
adj.	adjective
adv.	adverb
prep.	preposition

B. **Circle the correct word.**

1. A former resident (gave, given) this fountain to the city.

2. Was it the telephone or the doorbell that (rang, rung)?

3. Our guest speaker has (come, came) a little early.

4. Caroline has (know, known) Paul for ten years.

5. We asked Mom to (drive, driven) us to the movies.

6. Matt, haven't you (ate, eaten) the last piece of pineapple cake?

7. The frightened deer (ran, run) into the forest.

8. The Arnolds (gone, went) to Florida last January.

9. Andy (doesn't, don't) like to be late to work.

10. Chloe (took, taken) her brother to the zoo.

11. Susan (did, done) all of her chores before we went to the movie.

12. Jessica and I (is, are) ready to go, too.

13. Many of the trout (was, were) returned to the stream after the contest.

14. I have (began, begun) the study of Spanish.

15. A dead silence had (fell, fallen) upon the listeners.

16. Larry (wasn't, weren't) at work this morning.

A. Read the following paragraph.

> Amelia Earhart was born in Atchinson, Kansas, in 1897. She is one of the most famous American aviators. She was the first woman to fly solo across the Atlantic Ocean. At the time, 1932, air travel was a very rare occurrence, and it was even more unusual for women. With Earhart's example and encouragement, women were just beginning to break into aviation.
>
> One of her most daring flights was a solo trip from Hawaii to California in 1935. That journey was a longer and more dangerous flight than her European trip. However, it was for her attempted around-the-world flight in 1937 that most people remember Earhart. During this flight, her plane disappeared somewhere in the South Pacific. She and her co-pilot were never found. Many people believe she was working as an American spy to gather information on the Japanese war movement, but this idea has never been proven.

B. In the paragraph above, find three different pronouns and write them on the lines below.

1. _____   2. _____   3. _____

C. Find two proper adjectives and the nouns they describe.

1. _____   2. _____

D. Find two demonstrative adjectives and the nouns they describe.

1. _____   2. _____

E. Find two comparative adjectives.

1. _____   2. _____

F. Find six prepositional phrases.

1. _____

2. _____

3. _____

4. _____

5. _____

6. _____

G. Find three conjunctions.

1. _____   2. _____   3. _____

H. Rewrite the following paragraphs. Correct any mistakes in the use of possessive and plural nouns, pronouns, and verbs.

The first pilots of a motor-powered airplane was the Wright brothers, Orville and Wilbur. On December 17, 1903, the Wrights successfully flown their plane, Flyer I (which became known as Kitty Hawk), for the first time. The gasoline-powered plane were in the air for a total of 12 seconds. Another flight that day last 59 seconds and gone 852 feet.

The Wright brothers spent many years perfecting his airplane designs. Them were gifted engineer's and already has build printing machinery, bicycles, and gliders. Their breakthrough come when them observing the way a buzzard control their flight. Them continued to improve on its airplane designs over the next few years. They eventually sells the first military airplane to the United State Army in 1909. Eventually, European mechanic's produced more advanced airplane than the Wrights airplanes.

_____

_____

_____

_____

_____

_____

_____

_____

_____

_____

_____

_____

_____

_____

_____

_____

_____

_____

> ■ **Capitalize** the first word of a sentence and of each line of poetry.
>   EXAMPLES: Jim recited a poem in class. The first two lines follow.
>   All the animals looked up in wonder
>   When they heard the roaring thunder.
> ■ Capitalize the first word of a direct quotation.
>   EXAMPLE: Betty said, "Let's try to memorize a poem, too."
> ■ Capitalize the first, last, and all important words in the titles of books, poems, stories, and songs.
>   EXAMPLES: *The Jungle Book,* "The Children's Hour"

A. Circle each letter that should be capitalized. Write the capital letter above it.

1. Winston Churchill said, "the United States is the most powerful country in the world."

2. francis Scott Key wrote "the star spangled banner."

3. edgar Allen Poe, the author of "the raven," was born in Boston.

4. paul asked, "when do you plan to visit your pen pal?"

5. who wrote the poems "snowbound" and "the barefoot boy"?

6. what famous American said, "give me liberty, or give me death"?

> ■ Capitalize all **proper nouns.**
>   EXAMPLES: James T. White, Mom, Fifth Avenue, Italy, Missouri
>   Smokey Mountains, Thanksgiving, November, Statue of Liberty,
>   Boy Scouts of America, *Mayflower,* Texas State Fair
> ■ Capitalize all **proper adjectives.** A proper adjective is an adjective that is made from a proper noun.
>   EXAMPLES: the Italian language, Chinese food, French tourists

B. Circle each letter that should be capitalized. Write the capital letter above it.

1. Lauren, do your grandparents live in miami, florida, or atlanta, georgia?

2. The potomac river forms the boundary between virginia and maryland.

3. The *pinta,* the *niña,* and the *santa maría* were the ships columbus sailed.

4. The spanish explorers discovered the mississippi river before the english settlers

   landed at jamestown.

5. The founder of the american red cross was clara barton.

6. Glaciers are found in the rocky mountains, the alps mountains, and the andes mountains.

> ■ Capitalize a person's title when it comes before a name.
>   EXAMPLES: Mayor Flynn, Doctor Suarez, Governor Kuhn
> ■ Capitalize abbreviations of titles.
>   EXAMPLES: Ms. C. Cooke, Dr. Pearsoll, Gov. Milne, Judge Brenner

C. Circle each letter that should be capitalized. Write the capital letter above it.

1. How long have you been seeing dr. thompson?

2. Our class invited gov. thomas to speak at graduation.

3. dr. crawford w. long of Georgia is believed to be the first physician to

   use ether during surgery.

4. What time do you expect mr. and mrs. randall to arrive?

5. Most people believe senator dixon will win reelection.

6. It will be a close election unless gov. alden gives his support.

7. When is miss howell scheduled to begin teaching?

> ■ Capitalize abbreviations of days and months, parts of addresses, and
>   titles of members of the armed forces. Also capitalize all letters in the
>   abbreviations of states.
>   EXAMPLES: Tues.; Nov.; 201 S. Main St.; Maj. Donna C. Plunkett;
>   Boston, MA

D. Circle each letter that should be capitalized. Write the capital letter above it.

1. niles school art fair

   sat., feb. 8th, 9 A.M.

   110 n. elm dr.

2. austin water festival

   june 23–24

   mirror lake

   shoreville, mn 55108

3. october fest

   october 28 and 29

   9 A.M.–5 P.M.

   63 maple st.

4. sgt. barbara briggs

   1100 n. clarke st.

   detroit, mi

5. captain c. j. neil

   c/o *ocean star*

   p.o. box 4455

   portsmouth, nh 03801

6. dr. charles b. stevens

   elmwood memorial hospital

   1411 first street

   tucson, az 85062

E. Write a sentence to show each use of capital letters.

1. Name of a holiday _____

_____

2. Name of a restaurant in your community _____

_____

3. Name of a favorite book _____

_____

4. Name of an author _____

_____

5. Name of a business firm in or near your community _____

_____

6. Name of a country _____

_____

7. Name of a song _____

_____

8. Name of a magazine _____

_____

9. A direct quotation _____

_____

10. Name of a musician _____

_____

11. A title that is written as part of a name _____

_____

12. Name of a college or university _____

_____

13. Name of a river or lake _____

_____

14. Name of an actor or actress _____

_____

Using End Punctuation

60

- Use a **period** at the end of a declarative sentence.
  EXAMPLE: Sunlight is essential for the growth of plants.
- Use a **question mark** at the end of an interrogative sentence.
  EXAMPLE: How much sunlight does a plant need?

A. Use a period or question mark to end each sentence below.

1. Doesn't your uncle's family now live in Missouri____

2. "Snow Time" is a well-known poem____

3. Isn't someone knocking at the door, Beth____

4. Didn't Mrs. Newton ask us to meet her at 2:30 this afternoon____

5. In Yellowstone Park, we saw Morning Glory Pool, Handkerchief Pool, and Old Faithful____

6. The greatest library in ancient times was in Alexandria, Egypt____

7. Aren't the employees' checks deposited in a different bank____

8. Will Ms. Wilson start interviewing applicants at 10:00 A.M.____

9. My uncle has moved to Los Angeles, California____

10. Corn, oats, hay, and soybeans are grown in Iowa____

11. Isn't Alex the chairperson of our committee____

12. I've mowed the lawn, pulled the weeds, and raked the leaves____

13. Did the American Revolution begin on April 19, 1775____

14. Is El Salvador in Central America____

B. Add the correct end punctuation where needed in the paragraphs below.

Did you know that experts say dogs have been around for thousands of years____ In fact, they were the first animals to be made domestic____ The ancestors of dogs were hunters____ Wolves are related to domestic dogs____ Like wolves, dogs are social animals and prefer to travel in groups____ This is called pack behavior____

There have been many famous dogs throughout history____ Can you name any of them____ In the eleventh century, one dog, Saur, was named king of Norway____ The actual king was angry because his people had removed him from the throne, so he decided to make them subjects of the dog____ The first dog in space was a Russian dog named Laika____ Laika was aboard for the 1957 journey of *Sputnik*____ Most people have heard of Rin Tin Tin and Lassie____ These dogs became famous in movies and television____

There are several hundred breeds of dogs throughout the world____ The smallest is the Chihuahua____ A Chihuahua weighs less than two pounds____ Can you think of the largest____ A Saint Bernard or a Mastiff can weigh over 150 pounds____

78

Unit 4, Capitalization and Punctuation

> - Use a **period** at the end of an imperative sentence.
>   EXAMPLE: Open this jar of tomatoes for me, please.
> - Use an **exclamation point** at the end of an exclamatory sentence and after an interjection that shows strong feelings. If a command expresses great excitement, use an exclamation point at the end of the sentence.
>   EXAMPLES: Look at the stars! Ouch! I'm so excited!

C. Add periods or exclamation points where needed in these sentences below.

1. Answer the telephone, Michael____

2. Please clean the kitchen for me____

3. Oh____ I can't believe how late it is____

4. Hurry____ The plane is leaving in a few minutes____

5. Carry the bags to the check-in counter____

6. Then run to the waiting area____

7. Hold that seat for me____

8. I can't miss the flight____

9. Stop____ Stop____ You forgot your ticket____

10. Please slow down____

11. Sit down, and put on your seat belt____

12. We're off____

13. Look how small the city is____

14. Please put on your seat belt____

15. Obey the captain's orders____

16. I can't wait until we land____

17. Please give me that magazine____

18. Look____ We're about to land____

D. Add the correct end punctuation where needed in the paragraphs below.

Mr. Henry Modine lives in San Francisco____ He often exclaims, "What a wonderful town____" What do you think he does for a living____ Mr. Modine owns a fishing boat, *The Marlin*____ In all of San Francisco, there are few boats as fine as *The Marlin*____ Henry Modine named his boat after the fish his customers like the best—the marlin____ Henry practically guarantees his customers a fish or two if they come out on his boat____

"Fantastic____" shouts Henry when someone hooks a marlin____ Henry then says "Bring it in____" Part of Henry's job is to help the fishers reel in the big fish____ Can you believe that some marlins weigh 1,000 pounds or more____ Most of the ones Henry's customers catch weigh about 100 pounds____ They are either striped marlins or black marlins____

■ Use a **comma** between words or groups of words that are in a series.
  EXAMPLE: Pears, peaches, plums, and figs grow in the southern states.
■ Use a comma before a conjunction in a compound sentence.
  EXAMPLE: The farmers planted many crops, and they will work long hours to harvest them.
■ Use a comma after a subordinate clause when it begins a sentence.
  EXAMPLE: After we ate dinner, we went to a movie.

A. Add commas where needed in the sentences below.

1. Lois her sister and her brother all look forward to Lois's birthday each year.

2. It's Lois's birthday and it's a special day for another reason.

3. Lois Karen Alicia and Jenny are best friends.

4. Although they aren't the best musicians they are all in the band.

5. Karen is in the sixth grade and Jenny is in seventh.

6. Because the town's mayor always asks her Lois leads the Independence Day Parade.

7. It's because she was born July 4, 1975 and she is the only one in town with that birthday.

8. When it is time to begin the school band the baton twirlers and the football team follow Lois in the parade.

■ Use a comma to set off a quotation from the rest of a sentence.
  EXAMPLES: "I want to go with you," said Paul.
  Paul said, "I want to go with you."

B. Add commas before or after the quotations below.

1. "What a noise that rocket makes" said Liz.

2. Mark said "It's to announce Lois's birthday."

3. "It must be nice having a parade on your birthday" said Liz.

4. Lois answered "The best part is seeing everyone."

5. Mark asked "What about the cake?"

6. Lois said "You guessed my second favorite part."

7. "Hurray" yelled everyone, as a huge birthday cake with one hundred candles was brought out.

8. Lois said "This is the biggest cake yet".

9. The crowd yelled "Make a wish!"

10. Lois closed her eyes and thought "I wish for many more birthdays as wonderful as this one."

> ■ Use a comma to set off the name of a person who is being addressed.
>   EXAMPLE: Emily, are you ready to go?
> ■ Use a comma to set off words like yes, no, well, and oh at the beginning
>   of a sentence.
>   EXAMPLE: Yes, as soon as I find my jacket.
> ■ Use a comma to set off an appositive.
>   EXAMPLE: Felix, Emily's dog, is entered in a dog show.

C. Add commas where needed in the sentences below.

1. Mr. Taylor a grocery store owner was planning for a busy day.

2. "Diane would you open the store at 9 o'clock?" said Mr. Taylor.

3. "Of course that's the time we always open," said Diane.

4. "Pierre the chef at Elaine's will be coming by," he said.

5. Kelly said "Mr. Washington I'd like some fresh peanuts."

6. "Yes but how many pounds would you like?" answered Mr. Washington.

7. Mrs. Harmon asked "Mr. Todd what kind of fresh fruit do you have?"

8. "Well let me check what came in this afternoon," said Mr. Todd.

9. Alan the butcher had to wait on fifteen customers.

10. "I don't have time to wait Alan," said Carol.

11. The manager Mr. Gomez told everyone to be patient.

12. "Please it will go quickly if you all take a number," said Mr. Gomez.

13. "Yes you're right as usual," said the crowd.

14. Mr. Todd the produce manager went behind the counter to help.

15. Well they had sold all of their grapes and tomatoes before noon.

16. "We only have one bushel of green beans left" said Mr. Todd.

17. Mrs. Loster bought cherries bananas and corn.

18. She was planning a special dinner for Phil her husband.

19. Mrs. Loster spent the afternoon cooking baking and cleaning.

20. Today July 18 was his birthday.

D. Add commas where needed in the paragraph below.

Men women boys and girls from across the nation participate in the Special Olympics. Because of this event patterned after the Olympic games handicapped boys and girls have opportunities to compete in a variety of sports. The Special Olympics includes competition in track swimming and gymnastics. Volunteers plan carefully and they work hard to insure that the event will be challenging rewarding and worthwhile for all the participants. One of my neighbors Chris Bell once worked as a volunteer. "It was an experience that I'll never forget" he said.

> ■ Use **quotation marks** to show the exact words of a speaker. Use a comma or another punctuation mark to separate the quotation from the rest of the sentence. A quotation may be placed at the beginning or at the end of a sentence. Begin the quote with a capital letter.
> EXAMPLES: Pat said, "Please take the dog for a walk." "Please take the dog for a walk," said Mother.
> ■ A quotation may also be divided within the sentence.
> EXAMPLE: "Pat," said Scott, "I just returned from a walk!"

A. Add quotation marks and commas where needed in the sentences below.

1. Wait for me said Laurie because I want to go with you.

2. Kim, did you write an article about spacecraft? asked Tom.

3. Where is the manager's desk? inquired the stranger.

4. Mrs. Haynes asked What is Eric's address?

5. David asked How long did Queen Victoria rule the British Empire?

6. Carlos, did you bring your uncle's interesting article? asked Mrs. Stern.

7. Good morning said Cindy.

8. Doug asked Did Jim hurt himself when he fell?

9. The meeting begins in ten minutes said Rico.

10. Bob, you're early said Melissa.

11. Come on, said the coach you'll have to play harder to win this game!

12. Tony said, I know you'll do well in your new job. You're a hard worker.

> ■ Use an **apostrophe** in a contraction to show where a letter or letters have been taken out.
> EXAMPLES: I **can't** remember your name. **I'll** have to think about it.
> ■ Use an apostrophe to form a possessive noun. Add -'s to most singular nouns. Add -' to most plural nouns. Add -'s to a few nouns that have irregular plurals.
> EXAMPLES: **Dina's** house is made of brick. All the **neighbors'** houses are wooden. The **children's** treehouse is wooden.

B. Write the words in which an apostrophe has been left out. Insert apostrophes where they are needed.

1. Katie, didnt you want Sues job? _____

2. Havent you seen Pauls apartment? _____

3. Jim didnt hurt himself when he fell off Toms ladder. _____

4. The employees paychecks didnt arrive on time. _____

> ■ Use a **colon** after the greeting in a business letter.
>   EXAMPLES: Dear Mr. Johnson: Dear Sirs:
> ■ Use a colon between the hour and the minute when writing the time.
>   EXAMPLES: 1:30   6:15   11:47
> ■ Use a colon to introduce a list.
>   EXAMPLE: Our homework included the following assignments: ten
>   pages of reading, five multiple choice questions, and a brief essay.

A. Add colons where needed in the sentences below.

1. At 2 1 0 this afternoon, the meeting will start.

2. Please bring the following materials with you pencils, paper,

   erasers, and a notebook.

3. The meeting should be over by 4 3 0.

4. Those of you on the special committee should bring the following items cups,

   paper plates, forks, spoons, and napkins.

5. The meeting will deal with the following pool hours, swimming rules,

   and practice schedules.

6. The lifeguards will meet this evening from 8 0 0 to 1 0 0 0 to discuss responsibilities.

7. We will read the letter at 3 0 0 and have a question-and-answer session.

> ■ Use a **hyphen** between the parts of some compound words.
>   EXAMPLES: twenty-one   sister-in-law go-getter   well-behaved
>   air-conditioner middle-aged   sixty-six   great-grandfather
>   blue-green   old-fashioned second-story ninety-two
> ■ Use a hyphen to separate the syllables of a word that is carried over
>   from one line to the next.
>   EXAMPLE: When the coach has finished his speech, the class mem-
>   bers will be allowed to use the pool.

B. Add hyphens where needed in the sentences below.

1. Only fifty one students per semester are eligible for swimming lessons.

2. The entire seventh grade class will take swimming this year.

3. A water safety expert will give a series of classes on lifesaving.

4. The sign up sheet will be posted in the locker room.

5. The expert, Mr. Chambers, will speak at the next scheduled swim

   ming class.

6. The bookstore has seventy five copies of the lifesaving manual.

7. We will be tested on this on our year end exam.

8. All class members must pass the water safety exam.

A. Circle each letter that should be capitalized. Then add the correct end punctuation.

1. mr. j. c. moran owns a car dealership in chicago____

2. jesse decided to apply for a job on tuesday____

3. wow, mr. moran actually offered him a job____

4. jesse will start work in june____

5. jesse is the newest employee of moran's cars and vans____

6. didn't he get auto experience when he lived in minnesota____

7. he also got training at dunwoody technical institute____

B. Add punctuation where needed in the sentences below.

1. How did you get so lucky Jesse asked Mike.

2. It wasnt luck answered Jesse because I studied before I applied for this job.

3. How did you study to apply for a job Mike laughed.

4. I read an employment guide before I applied answered Jesse.

5. Wow thats something exclaimed Mike.

6. Its a great employment guide Jesse added.

7. It says if you really want to get a job, you should do the following be neat be on time be polite and be enthusiastic.

8. Arent there some part time jobs available asked Mike.

9. Jesse said Why dont you read my guide and get ready for an interview?

C. Punctuate the letter below. Circle each letter that should be capitalized.

73 E. river st.

waterton, me 32540

june 7, 1989

Dear mr. moran,

    I just wanted to thank you for offering me the part time job____ Tom told me that i would be doing the following things cleaning the service area adjusting cars brakes keeping the tools in order and changing oil____ i promise to do these jobs carefully and thoroughly____ he also told me to read *mechanics manual*____ ill do that before I start next monday____ Do you know what____ i cant wait to start____

Sincerely yours,

jesse sanchez

A. Circle each letter that should be capitalized below. Add punctuation where needed.

720 w. ravin

newland, va 27890

may 4, 1989

Dear Sirs,

on may 3, 1989, i received the tape player i had ordered from your catalog___ the following pieces were missing from the package the earphones the high quality cassette tape and the adapter___ please let me know what i should do about this___ will you send the pieces or should I return the whole package___ since your motto is that customers happiness is your goal i thought i would let you know that im not very happy about this___ ive ordered other things in the past___ they were great___ what happened to my order this time___ im waiting anxiously for your answer___

Sincerely yours,

bonita williams

B. Circle each letter that should be capitalized. Add punctuation where needed.

478 n. beacon

trainor, in 73210

june 1, 1989

Dear ms. williams,

please excuse us___ this is awful___ do send the entire package back and we will replace it___ how can we apologize properly___ first, we will send your new tape player special delivery so you will get it quickly___ second, we will enclose a copy of sounds of the eighties for your pleasure___ we are sorry___ thank you for your past orders___ our customers happiness is our major goal___ well do everything we can to make sure that this order goes through properly___ please let us know if everythings there___ we look forward to hearing from you___

Gratefully yours,

the sound team

C. Rewrite the letter below. Capitalize any letters that should be capitalized. Add needed punctuation.

720 w. raven

newland, va 27890

june 27, 1989

Dear sound team,

hurray____ my tape player arrived today and its great____ thank you____ now when I walk my dog i can listen to a tape____ thank you also for sounds of the eighties____ can you believe it____ i have a copy of tunes of the seventies and had planned to buy sounds of the eighties____ now i dont have to____ thats great____

I also want to thank you for your courteous letter____ im sure mistakes can happen to anyone____ everyones quick action was greatly appreciated____ your letter and package arrived at 10 00 this morning____ youre fantastic____

Sincerely,

bonita williams

_____

_____

_____

_____

_____

_____

_____

_____

_____

_____

_____

_____

_____

_____

_____

Writing Sentences

> - Every sentence has a base consisting of a simple subject and a simple predicate.
>   EXAMPLE: <u>Mandy</u> <u>baked</u>.
> - Expand the meaning of a sentence by adding adjectives, adverbs, and prepositional phrases to the sentence base.
>   EXAMPLE: **My cousin** Mandy baked **a delicious orange cake for dessert.**

A. Expand the meaning of each sentence base by adding adjectives, adverbs, and/or prepositional phrases. Write each expanded sentence below.

1. (Carl swam.)

   _____

2. (Clock ticked.)

   _____

3. (Snow falls.)

   _____

4. (Sun rose.)

   _____

5. (Fireworks exploded.)

   _____

B. Imagine two different scenes for each sentence base below. Write an expanded sentence to describe each scene you imagine.

1. (Students listened.) **a.** _____

   b. _____

2. (Jason wrote.) **a.** _____

   b. _____

3. (Gene played.) **a.** _____

   b. _____

4. (Dad drove.) **a.** _____

   b. _____

5. (We helped.) **a.** _____

   b. _____

> ■ A **topic sentence** states the main idea of a paragraph. It is often placed at the beginning of a paragraph.
>
> EXAMPLE:
>
> **Mario was asked to write an article about the new recreation center for the school paper.** He wrote a list of questions to ask. He interviewed the park superintendent. He found out about the old park and why it was necessary to build a recreation center.

A. Underline the topic sentence in each paragraph below.

1. Mario knew that having good questions was very important to a successful interview. He thought carefully about what he wanted to know. Then he divided his questions into groups. Some were about the building. Some were about recreation. Others were about the staff.

2. He wanted to include something about the history of the park. He found out who first owned the land. He also asked how people had used the park over the years.

3. Mario found out that the park was nearly as old as the town itself. It had been the scene of picnics, baseball games, carnivals, concerts, and holiday festivals. Political meetings had also been held there.

B. Write a topic sentence for each group of sentences below.

1. Topic Sentence: _____

    a. Mr. Leland was the park superintendent.
    b. He had worked in the field of recreation and sports all his adult life.
    c. His father had been a high school teacher and coach.
    d. His grandfather had been a popular baseball player.

2. Topic Sentence: _____

    a. Mario enjoyed talking to Mr. Leland.
    b. He found out more than he had ever expected.
    c. Mr. Leland told him why the community needed the center.
    d. The city had grown, and it needed to provide recreation for its residents.

C. Think of a topic you are interested in. Write the topic on the line. Then write a topic sentence.

Topic: _____

Topic Sentence: _____

_____

> ■ The idea expressed in the topic sentence can be developed with sentences containing **supporting details.** Details can include facts, examples, and reasons.

A. Circle the topic sentence, and underline only the sentences containing supporting details in the paragraph below.

Mario asked Theresa to help him with the article. She would write out the tape-recorded interviews. She would also make suggestions for changes. Theresa is very pretty. Finally, they would both work on typing the article.

B. After each topic sentence, write five sentences containing supporting details.

1. You must be organized when writing an article.

a. _____

b. _____

c. _____

d. _____

e. _____

2. It is important to learn all you can about your topic.

a. _____

b. _____

c. _____

d. _____

e. _____

C. Write four sentences that contain supporting details for the topic sentence you wrote in Exercise C, page 88.

Topic Sentence: _____

a. _____

b. _____

c. _____

d. _____

- One way to organize information in a paragraph is to put it in **chronological order**—the time in which events occurred. Words such as first, next, second, then, finally, and later are used to indicate the order in which events happen.   EXAMPLE: **First,** Mario checked his tape recorder. **Then** he left for the interview.
- Another way to organize information is to use **spatial order.** Words such as above, near, over, beside, right, left, closer, farther, up, and down are used to express spatial relationships.   EXAMPLE: The bald eagle sat on **top** of the tree. He watched the pond **below.**

A. Read each paragraph below and tell whether it is in chronological order or spatial order. For the paragraph in chronological order, underline the time order words. For the paragraph in spatial order, underline the words that indicate spatial order.

1.   The park board of directors must first approve the architect's design for the recreation center. Then they must develop and approve a budget for the construction of the center. Finally, they can give approval to construction of the center.

Order: _____

2.   The plan for the recreation center includes play areas for young children. A slide and swingset will be built next to a large sand box. A jungle gym will be to the left of the slide. Children will be able to climb to the top of the jungle gym and then jump down to the ground.

Order: _____

B. Number the details below in chronological order.

_____ Then early in March, the park board of directors approved the architect's design.

_____ Next, the budget was approved in April.

_____ The center's roof was finally completed in August.

_____ In January, the architect first finished his design.

C. Choose one of the scenes below. Write a paragraph of at least four sentences describing the scene. Use spatial order words to show location.

Scenes: your house, a ballpark, a restaurant, a theater, a friend's house

_____

_____

_____

_____

Topic and Audience

- The **topic** of a story or an article is the subject written about.
- The **audience** is the group of readers.
  EXAMPLES: students, family members, neighbors, readers of a newspaper

A. Choose the most likely audience for each topic listed below.

      a. first-graders   **b.** the city council   **c.** high-school students   **d.** parents

_____ 1. Star Athlete Visits Students at Recreation Center

_____ 2. Study Shows Connection between Time Spent Exercising and Student Progress in School

_____ 3. Peter Rabbit Here for Hop and Jump Exercises

_____ 4. Council Considers Tax Plans to Finance Recreation Center

_____ 5. Tryouts for High School Track Team on Friday

_____ 6. Study Shows City Budget Shortfall Next Year

_____ 7. Kelsey School Parents' Night Next Thursday

_____ 8. Officer Safety to Visit Young Students Next Week

_____ 9. State University Considers Raising Tuition

_____ 10. Governor Approves Funds to Expand City Bus Service

B. Read the paragraph below. Then answer the questions that follow.

On Tuesday evening, May 2, 1988, at 6:00, Hawkeye, the mascot of the Child Protection Foundation, will be at the park with his handler, Officer Roy Meyers. While Hawkeye, the long-eared hound, entertains the youngsters, Officer Meyers will discuss the topic "Keeping Your Children Safe." This unusual pair has traveled across the state to introduce the findings on topics such as accidents in the home, hazardous toys, and bike safety.

1. What is the topic of the paragraph?

_____

2. Name two possible audiences for the paragraph.

_____

3. Explain why each audience might be interested.

Audience 1: _____

Audience 2: _____

C. Choose a topic in which you are interested. Write the name of the topic, and name the audience it would be most likely to interest.

Topic: _____

Audience: _____

■ A **clustering diagram** shows how ideas relate to a particular topic. The topic is written in the center. Related ideas are written around the topic. Lines show the connections between the ideas.

EXAMPLE:

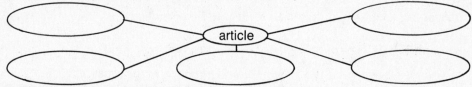

establishment — park — political meetings
holidays — carnivals
picnics

Topic Sentence: The recreation center will be built on land that was once a park.

A. Read each paragraph below. Notice the underlined topic sentence as you read. Then fill in each cluster to show how the details relating to that topic sentence could have been chosen.

1.   Mario had a lot of work to do for the article. He had to finish the interviews, decide what information to use, and write a rough draft. He then had to revise the draft, type the final copy, and proofread it.

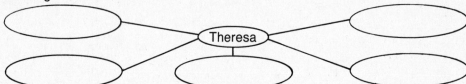

article

2.   Theresa worked hard on the article. She typed the interviews. She edited the article. She organized the rough draft. Finally, she helped with the final revision and proofreading.

Theresa

B. Rewrite the topic sentence you wrote on page 89, Exercise C.

Topic Sentence: _____

C. Write that topic from Exercise B in the center of the cluster below. Then fill in the cluster with details that would support your main topic.

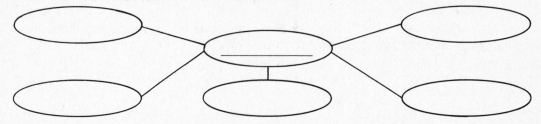

■ Before you write about a topic, organize your thoughts by making an **outline.** An outline consists of the title of the topic, **main headings** for the main ideas, and **subheadings** for supporting ideas.

■ Main headings are listed after Roman numerals. Subheadings are listed after capital letters.

Topic: The need for a recreation center

I. Problems with park
  A. Age of equipment
  B. Limited usefulness for residents
II. Advantages of recreation center
  A. Wide range of uses
  B. Safe, up-to-date equipment

■ **Refer to your topic sentence on page 92, Exercise B. Write an outline based on the clusters, using the example outline as a guide.**

Topic: _____

  I. _____

    A. _____

    B. _____

  II. _____

    A. _____

    B. _____

  III. _____

    A. _____

    B. _____

  IV. _____

    A. _____

    B. _____

  V. _____

    A. _____

    B. _____

> - Writers use interviews to get information. Good interview questions will encourage the person being interviewed to talk freely about the subject.
>   EXAMPLES: Why do we need a recreation center? Who will be involved in making decisions?
> - Avoid questions that can be answered either <u>yes</u> or <u>no</u> by beginning them with words such as <u>who</u>, <u>what</u>, <u>why</u>, and <u>how</u>.
>   EXAMPLE: Why do we need a recreation center?

A. Write <u>who</u>, <u>what</u>, <u>when</u>, <u>where</u>, <u>why</u>, or <u>how</u> to complete each question.

1. _____ will vote on the budget for the recreation center?

2. _____ will be the various uses of the center?

3. _____ will the center be paid for?

4. _____ will the center be located?

5. _____ do you think a recreation center is necessary?

6. _____ will the center be completed?

B. Rewrite the questions below so that they cannot be answered <u>yes</u> or <u>no</u>.

1. Does the park have an interesting history?

   _____

2. Is the location of the park good?

   _____

3. Does the council have plans to raise local taxes?

   _____

4. Will the townspeople have a say on the new recreation center?

   _____

C. Choose a topic and write three questions about it. Remember to begin each question with <u>who</u>, <u>what</u>, <u>when</u>, <u>where</u>, <u>how</u>, or <u>why</u>.

Topic: _____

1. _____

2. _____

3. _____

■ Many factual articles are based on information gathered in an interview. The writer asks questions about the subject he or she wants to cover and then uses the information to write an article.

■ **Read the notes from the interview. Then read the paragraph that Mario and Theresa wrote, and answer the questions that follow.**

Question 1: Mr. Leland, how do you feel about the proposed recreation center?

Answer: It is definitely needed. The park is too small for our growing city and needs massive repairs anyway. It will be good for the whole city to have a well-equipped recreation center.

Question 2: Your family has been involved in sports for many years. How do you feel about the modern approach to physical fitness for people of all ages?

Answer: Physical fitness is vital for everyone. That's why the new recreation center is so important. It will offer facilities and programs for everyone, regardless of age or current fitness levels.

Question 3: What will the recreation center include?

Answer: The center will house an indoor pool, a small ice rink, two gyms, meeting rooms, arts-and-crafts facilities, and locker rooms with showers. We also hope to include a weight-lifting room.

According to Mr. Tom Leland, park superintendent, the new recreation center will be a welcome addition to the city's facilities. The old park is now outdated and can no longer fill the needs of the people. Mr. Leland recommends that the park be the site of the new recreation center. Its facilities, which will include an indoor pool and two gyms, will fit everyone's needs, regardless of age or current fitness levels.

1. Does the author quote Mr. Leland exactly? _____

2. Write one sentence in the article that came from question 1.

_____

_____

3. Write one sentence in the article that came from question 3.

_____

_____

4. Write another question that Mario could have asked Mr. Leland.

_____

5. What other things will the recreation center include that were not in the article?

_____

- **Revising** gives you a chance to rethink and review what you have written and to improve your writing. Revise by adding words and information, by taking out unneeded words and information, and by moving words, sentences, and paragraphs around.
- **Proofreading** has to do with checking spelling, punctuation, grammar, and capitalization. Use proofreader's marks to show changes needed in your writing.

Proofreader's Marks

Take something out.

Capitalize.

Add a period.

Correct spelling.

Make a small letter.

Add quotation marks.

Indent for new paragraph.

Add a comma.

Add something.

Move something.

A. Rewrite the paragraph below. Correct the errors by following the proofreader's marks.

The berryton city council today appruved plans today for construction of a New recreation center mayor june booth said the center to be located on the sight of the currant adams park will provide berryton residents with a variety of recreational programs" the center's facilities include will an indoor pool to gymnasiums, arts-and-crafts facilities, and a small ice rink and an indoor pool Several meating rooms will also be Included too for use buy various organizations.

_____

_____

_____

_____

_____

_____

_____

_____

B. Read the paragraphs below. Use proofreader's marks to revise and proofread the paragraphs. Then write your revised paragraphs below.

Representatives from severals community organizations attended the meeting to express their support of the recreation center "Construction of this center Is Long Overdue Are members will now have a central place in which to meat instead of crowding into each others homes said Milton Sayre chairman of the berryton citizens senior league

plans call for a groundbreaking ceremony on thursday may 16 at 2 30 followed by a reception in adams park Construction is scheduled mayor booth supervisor john leland and city council members will participate all residents are invited to join them at the ceremoney

_____

_____

_____

_____

_____

_____

_____

_____

_____

_____

_____

_____

_____

_____

_____

A. Number the following sentences in chronological order. Circle any words that indicate chronological order.

_____ Next, he looked for Tony's name.

_____ He ran to tell Tony the good news.

_____ First, Jason ran to the bulletin board to look for the team lineup.

_____ Then he looked for his name and position.

B. Read the paragraph below. Then circle the topic sentence, and underline only the supporting details.

> The annual Springfest bike race was held at the county fairgrounds. Kathy Richards didn't seem to mind that she was one of only two girls in this year's bike race. Kathy took the lead early. She handled the course with ease and skill. Kathy is an excellent student. Her winning time set a new record for the race. Everyone congratulated Kathy.

C. Complete the cluster for the topic given in the center.

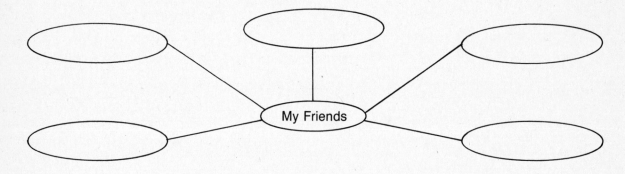

My Friends

D. Begin an outline based on that cluster.

Topic: My Friends

I. _____

    A. _____

    B. _____

II. _____

    A. _____

    B. _____

A. Choose a topic in which you are interested.

_____

B. Decide who your audience will be.

_____

C. Write a topic sentence.

_____

D. Draw a cluster diagram for your topic. Draw more circles for supporting details if necessary.

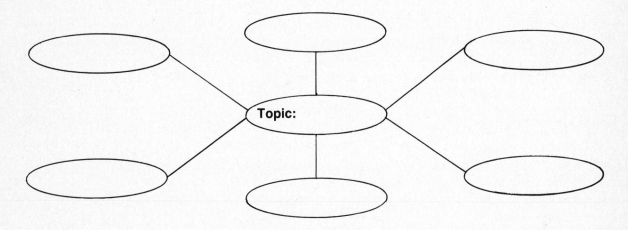

E. Write a short outline for a report on your topic.

I. _____

    A. _____

    B. _____

II. _____

    A. _____

    B. _____

III. _____

    A. _____

    B. _____

F. Write five questions about your topic that you would ask if you had an interview with someone who is an expert on the subject.

1. _____

2. _____

3. _____

4. _____

5. _____

G. Write a paragraph with a topic sentence and at least five sentences containing supporting details. Then revise and proofread your paragraph.

_____

_____

_____

_____

_____

_____

_____

H. Rewrite the paragraph below. Correct the errors by following the proofreader's marks. Use the proofreader's marks on page 96 if necessary.

One of the most importantest peaces of fire savety equipment is the smoke detector. The smoke detector continually all the time monitors the air in you're house. it sounds an alarm at the first sign of trouble. Fire officials consider the smoke detectors won of the most best effective low-cost devices alarms available Today.

_____

_____

_____

_____

_____

_____

_____

> - A **dictionary** is a reference book that contains definitions of words and other information about their history and use.
> - **Entries** in a dictionary are listed in **alphabetical order.**
> - **Guide words** appear at the top of each dictionary page. Guide words show the first and last entry on the page.
>   EXAMPLE: The word <u>lease</u> would appear on a dictionary page with the guide words <u>learn</u> / <u>lesson</u>. The word <u>lever</u> would not.

A. Put a check in front of each word that would be listed on a dictionary page with the given guide words.

1. fade / flat

_____ faster

_____ face

_____ flavor

_____ fetch

_____ flatter

_____ factory

_____ flag

_____ fancy

_____ flop

_____ fertile

_____ flow

_____ flame

2. image / inform

_____ information

_____ impossible

_____ insect

_____ incomplete

_____ ignore

_____ immense

_____ indeed

_____ improve

_____ insist

_____ infect

_____ imagine

_____ inherit

3. radio / reach

_____ rail

_____ rabbit

_____ ranch

_____ real

_____ raw

_____ raccoon

_____ raft

_____ read

_____ ramp

_____ rate

_____ reduce

_____ rake

B. Number the words in each column in the order of their appearance in a dictionary. Then write the words that could be the guide words for each column.

1. _____ / _____

_____ bedroom

_____ blend

_____ blame

_____ biography

_____ block

_____ blink

_____ bear

_____ benefit

_____ believe

_____ beach

2. _____ / _____

_____ dine

_____ depend

_____ determine

_____ department

_____ district

_____ disease

_____ disturb

_____ discard

_____ difference

_____ dessert

3. _____ / _____

_____ fire

_____ face

_____ free

_____ finger

_____ faint

_____ flower

_____ family

_____ follow

_____ fair

_____ flavor

> - A **syllable** is a part of a word that is pronounced at one time. Dictionary entry words are divided into syllables to show how they can be divided at the end of a writing line.
> - A **hyphen** (-) is placed between syllables to separate them.
>   EXAMPLE: quar-ter-back
> - If a word has a beginning or ending syllable of only one letter, do not divide it so that one letter stands alone.
>   EXAMPLES: a-fraid   bus-y

A. Find each word in a dictionary. Then write each word with a hyphen between each syllable.

1. allowance _____

2. porridge _____

3. hostess _____

4. peddle _____

5. character _____

6. hickory _____

7. solution _____

8. variety _____

9. talent _____

10. weather _____

11. brilliant _____

12. enthusiasm _____

13. dramatic _____

14. employment _____

15. laboratory _____

16. judgment _____

17. kingdom _____

18. recognize _____

19. usual _____

20. yesterday _____

B. Write two ways in which each word may be divided at the end of a writing line.

1. victorious _____ vic-torious _____ _____ victori-ous _____

2. inferior _____ _____

3. quantity _____ _____

4. satisfactory _____ _____

5. security _____ _____

6. possession _____ _____

7. thermometer _____ _____

8. getaway _____ _____

- Each dictionary entry word is followed by a respelling that shows how the word is **pronounced**.
- An **accent mark** follows a syllable that is said with extra stress. In some words more than one syllable is stressed. The syllable that receives primary stress is followed by a **primary accent mark (′)**. The syllable that receives secondary stress is followed by a **secondary accent mark (′)**.
    EXAMPLE: sub·sti·tute (sub′ stə tūt′)
- A **pronunciation key** (shown below) explains the other symbols used in the respellings.

A. Use the pronunciation key to answer the questions.

1. How many words are given for the symbol ə? _____

2. What symbol is used for the sound of the s in treasure? _____

3. What symbol would be used for the sound of a in bar? _____

4. What symbol would be used for the sound of wh in whether? _____

5. What symbol would be used for the sound of a in around? _____

6. What symbol would be used for the sound of oo in hoot? _____

> at; āpe; fär; câre; end; mē; it; īce; pîerce; hot; ōld; sông; fôrk; oil; out; up; ūse; rüle; pùll; tûrn; chin; sing; shop; thin; this; hw in white; zh in treasure. The symbol ə stands for the unstressed vowel sound in about, taken, pencil, lemon, and circus.

B. Use the pronunciation key to help you choose the correct word for each respelling. Underline the correct word.

1. (hēl)   hail   heel   hole
2. (ī′ vē)   ivy   I've   eve
3. (thā)   thee   they   the
4. (let′ ər)   letter   lighter   litter
5. (kāp)   cap   cop   cape
6. (ri tīr′)   retort   retire   writer
7. (ri trēt′)   retreat   retread   retrial
8. (sap)   soap   sip   sap
9. (doun)   den   down   dawn
10. (nū)   no   now   new
11. (hīt)   hit   height   hate
12. (noiz)   nosy   nose   noise
13. (wāt)   what   wit   weight
14. (dī′ mənd)   diamond   demand   depend
15. (ī′ ərn)   horn   earn   iron
16. (lēd)   loud   lead   load

- A dictionary lists the **definitions** of each entry word. Many words have more than one definition. In this case, the most commonly used definition is given first. Sometimes a definition is followed by a sentence showing a use of the entry word.
- A dictionary also gives the **part of speech** for each entry word. An abbreviation (shown below) stands for each part of speech. Some words may be used as more than one part of speech.
  EXAMPLE: **mess** (mes) *n.* **1.** an untidy, usually dirty, condition. *-v.* to make untidy and dirty.

- **Use the dictionary samples below to answer the questions.**

cage (kāj) *n.* a structure in which animals can be kept. *v.* to lock up or keep in a cage.
cos-tume (kos′ tōōm) *n.* **1.** an outfit worn in pretending to be someone else: *Karla's costume was the nicest one in the play.* **2.** a type of dress associated with a particular people, place or time. *-v.* to provide with a costume.

cot-ton (kot′ ən) *n.* **1.** soft fibers that grow in a cluster on seed pods of certain plants and are used to make cloth. **2.** the plant on which these fibers grow. **3.** thread made from cotton fibers. **4.** cloth woven of cotton. *-adj.* made of cotton: *The cotton dress might shrink in warm water.*

1. Which words can be used as either a noun

   or a verb? _____

2. Which word can be used as an adjective?

   _____

3. Which word has the most meanings?

   _____

n.	noun
pron.	pronoun
v.	verb
adj.	adjective
adv.	adverb
prep.	preposition

4. Which word can be used as a noun or as an adjective? _____

5. Write the most commonly used definition of costume. _____

   _____

6. Write a sentence in which you use cage as a verb. _____

   _____

7. Write a sentence using the first definition of costume. _____

   _____

8. Use the second definition of cotton in a sentence. _____

   _____

- An **etymology** tells of an entry word's origin and development. Many dictionary entries include an etymology.
- The etymology is usually enclosed in brackets [ ] after the definition of the entry word. The language from which the entry word came into English is listed first, followed by the language from which that word came, and so on. Often the symbol < is used to save space and stands for the phrase "is derived from" or "comes from."

  EXAMPLE: **tu-lip** (too′ lip, tyoo′ lip) [Lat. *Tulipa* < Turk. *tülibend,* turban < Pers. *dulband.*] The word *tulip* came into English from the New Latin word *Tulipa,* which came from the Turkish word *tülibend,* which meant "turban." The word *tülibend* came from the Persian word *dulband.*

■ **Use the dictionary samples below to answer the questions.**

e-mo-tion (i mō′ shən) *n.* strong feeling. [Middle French *emouvoir* to stir up, from Latin *exmovēre* to move away, disturb from *ex* + *movēre* to move.]

gup-py (gup′ ē) *n.* a small, brightly-colored freshwater fish. [After R. J. L. Guppy (1836–1916), who introduced the fish to England.]

line (līn) *n.* a long, narrow mark as with pen or pencil. [A combination of Old French *ligne* string, cord and Old English *line* cord, rope.]

load (lōd) *n.* **1.** that which is put on a pack animal to carry. **2.** cargo put on a ship, plane, train, or truck. [Middle English *lod,* from Old English *lād* support, carrying.]

mar-a-thon (mar′ a thon′) *n.* a cross-country foot race. [After *Marathon,* Greece (so called because in 490 B.C. a messenger ran from Marathon to Athens to announce a victory over the Persians).]

1. Which word comes from the name of a person? _____

2. Which word originally meant "to move"? _____

3. Which languages are in the history of the word line? _____

4. Which word comes from both Middle English and Old English? _____

5. Which word comes from the name of a place? _____

6. Which words have more than one language in their histories? _____

7. What is the meaning of the Latin word exmovēre? _____

8. Why is the guppy named after R. J. L. Guppy? _____

9. What did the Middle English word lod come from? _____

10. Why do we call a long race a marathon? _____

_____

11. Which word comes from a word that meant "support or carrying"? _____

12. Which word comes from the word ligne? _____

13. Which words come from French? _____

Using Parts of a Book

> - A **title page** lists the name of a book and its author.
> - A **copyright page** tells who published the book, where it was published, and when it was published.
> - A **table of contents** lists the chapter or unit titles and the page numbers on which they begin. It is at the front of a book.
> - An **index** gives a detailed list of the topics in a book and the page numbers on which each topic is found. It is in the back of a book.

A. Answer the questions below.

1. Where should you look for the page number of a particular topic? _____

2. Where should you look to find out who wrote a book? _____

3. Where should you look to get a general idea of the contents of a book? _____

4. Where should you look to find out when a book was published? _____

5. Where should you look to find the name of the book? _____

6. Where should you look to find out who published a book? _____

B. Use your *Language Exercises* book to answer the questions.

1. What company published this book? _____

2. How many units are in this book? _____

3. On what page does Unit 2 start? _____

4. Where is the index located? _____

5. What is the copyright date? _____

6. What pages contain lessons on pronouns? _____

7. On what page does Unit 5 start? _____

8. On what pages are the lessons on commas found? _____

9. What lesson is on page 89? _____

10. List the pages that teach prepositions. _____

11. On what page is the lesson on guide words found? _____

12. On what page is the lesson on prefixes found? _____

13. On what page does Unit 3 start? _____

- A **chart** lists information in columns, which you read down, and rows, which you read across. The information can be either words or numbers.
- A **graph** shows how quantities change over time. It often shows how two or more things change in relation to one another. The information can be shown through the use of lines, dots, bars, pictures, or in a circle.

■ **Use the chart and the graph to answer the following questions.**

Library Use Chart

Day of the Week	Science Students	History Students
Monday	18	5
Tuesday	22	16
Wednesday	14	10
Thursday	4	20
Friday	13	15

Library Use Graph

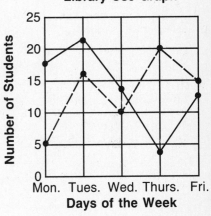

Graph Key
Science students _____
History students _ _ _

1. How many science students used the library on Monday? _____ on Tuesday? _____

   on Wednesday? _____ on Thursday? _____ on Friday? _____

2. Can the question in number 1 be answered by studying the Library Use Chart? _____

   the Library Use Graph? _____

3. On which day was the number of science and history students using the library

   nearly the same? _____

4. On which day did the most science and history students use the library? _____

5. How many science and history students used the library on the day

   mentioned in number 4? _____

6. On which day did the least number of science and history students use the library? _____

- The **card catalog** contains information cards on every book in the library. Some libraries are now computerized and have no card catalogs, but the information in the computer is filed in the same manner as the information in the card catalog.
- Each book has three cards in the catalog. The cards are filed separately according to: 1. the author's last name, 2. the subject of the book, and 3. the title of the book.
- Most smaller libraries use the **Dewey Decimal System** to organize their books. Each book is assigned a **call number** from 000 to 999, according to its subject matter.

A. Refer to the sample catalog card to answer the questions about one book.

Subject Card

Call number — 973.3 **American Revolution** — Subject

Author — **Martin, Joseph Plumb,** 1760–1850.

Title — Yankee doodle boy: a young soldier's adventures in the American Revolution, told by himself. Edited by George F. Scheer. With maps & illus. by Victor Mays. New York, — Place published

Publisher — W. R. Scott (1964) — Date published

Number of pages — 190 p. illus. — Illustrated

1. What is the title? _____

2. Who is the author? _____

3. Who published it? _____ When was it published? _____

4. What is the call number? _____ How many pages does it have? _____

5. What is the general subject? _____

6. Does it contain maps and illustrations? _____

B. Write author, title, or subject to tell which card you would look for to locate the book or books.

1. books about mountain climbing _____

2. *Life in the Chinese Countryside* _____

3. a book of short stories by O. Henry _____

4. a book by Jane Austen _____

■ An **encyclopedia** is a reference book that contains articles on many different topics. The articles are arranged alphabetically in volumes. Each volume is marked to show which articles are inside.

■ Guide words are used to show the first topic on each page.

■ At the end of most articles there is a listing of **cross-references** to related topics for the reader to investigate.

■ Most encyclopedias also have an index of subject titles.

A. Find the entry for <u>Knute Rockne</u> in an encyclopedia. Then answer the following questions.

1. What encyclopedia did you use? _____

2. When did Knute Rockne live? _____

3. Where was he born? _____

4. Where did he go to college? _____

5. For what is he best known? _____

B. Find the entry for <u>Redwood</u> in an encyclopedia. Then answer the following questions.

1. What encyclopedia did you use? _____

2. Where does the redwood tree grow? _____

3. By what other name is it known? _____

4. What is special about this tree? _____

5. How tall do most redwoods grow? _____

C. Find the entry in an encyclopedia for a person in whom you are interested. Then answer the following questions.

1. Who is your subject? _____

2. What encyclopedia did you use? _____

3. When did the person live? _____

4. Where did the person live? _____

5. What is it about the person that makes him or her famous? _____

_____

6. What cross-references are listed? _____

> ■ A **thesaurus** is a reference book that writers use to find the exact words they need. Like a dictionary, a thesaurus lists its entry words alphabetically. Each entry word has a list of **synonyms (syn.),** or words that can be used in its place. Some thesauruses also include **antonyms (ant.)** for each entry word.
>
> EXAMPLE: You have just written the following sentence: I was so hungry that I **ate** my lunch quickly. With the help of a thesaurus you could improve your sentence by replacing ate with a more specific synonym, such as devoured. I was so hungry that I **devoured** my lunch quickly.

A. Refer to the sample thesaurus entry below to answer the questions.

> **difficult** *adj.* ***syn.*** puzzling, complex, awkward ***ant.*** simple, effortless

1. Which is the entry word? _____

2. What are its synonyms? _____

3. Which word would you use to describe something complicated? _____

4. Which word would you use to describe something baffling? _____

5. Which word would you use to describe something that might be embarrassing? _____

6. What are the antonyms of difficult? _____

7. Which antonym would you use to describe a test that is easy? _____

B. Use one of the synonyms of difficult to complete each sentence.

1. As an engineer, Marie designs very _____ pieces of machinery.

2. We found ourselves in a very _____ situation when we arrived too early.

3. Manuel is very good at solving _____ mysteries.

C. Write three sentences, each containing a different synonym of difficult.

1. _____

_____

2. _____

_____

3. _____

_____

D. Study the thesaurus entry for <u>talk</u>. Then use a synonym of <u>talk</u> to complete each sentence.

> **talk** *v. syn.* mention, chat, discuss, whisper, argue, describe, grumble, say

1. Out of courtesy to others, you should always _____ in a movie theater.

2. Please _____ your house so that I can find it easily.

3. If you must _____, you should try not to lose your temper.

4. My dad often likes to _____ with his college buddies.

5. Can we _____ the new proposal some time?

6. You always know the right thing to_____.

7. My little brothers always _____ when they're tired and cranky.

8. Did I _____ that I will be gone tomorrow?

E. Write five sentences, each containing a different synonym of <u>talk</u>.

1. _____

2. _____

3. _____

4. _____

5. _____

F. Circle the synonym that best completes each sentence.

1. The batter (looked, glared) at the umpire after his bad call.

2. The (noise, roar) of the crowd was deafening.

3. My younger brother (aged, matured) after he got to junior high school.

4. My friends often (accumulate, gather) at the park after school.

5. The man used a (knife, blade) to cut the freshly baked bread.

6. It is my (judgment, opinion) that we all need a vacation now and then.

7. I felt a (loop, knot) in my stomach as I walked up the aisle.

8. I can almost (imagine, think) what it would be like to fly.

9. I (knocked, pushed) the vase over, and water spilled on the floor.

10. School had begun when the tornado (alarm, bell) sounded.

11. I (floated, drifted) to sleep while reading last night.

12. I will miss our cottage after we (leave, abandon) it for the year.

13. We (disguised, hid) our friend's present in her locker.

■ The ***Readers' Guide to Periodical Literature*** lists by author and by subject all the articles that appear in nearly two hundred magazines. Use the *Readers' Guide* when you need
- Recent articles on a particular subject,
- Several articles written over a period of time about the same subject,
- Many articles written by the same author.

■ **Use the *Readers' Guide* samples to answer the questions.**

Subject Entry

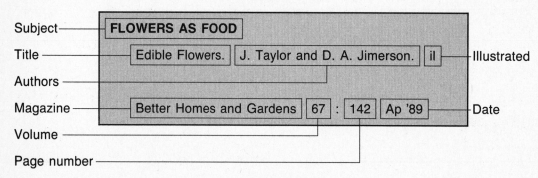

Subject ——— **FLOWERS AS FOOD**

Title ——— Edible Flowers. | J. Taylor and D. A. Jimerson. | il ——— Illustrated

Authors

Magazine ——— Better Homes and Gardens | 67 | : | 142 | Ap '89 ——— Date

Volume

Page number

Author Entry

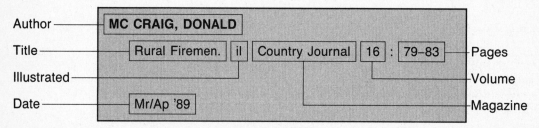

Author ——— **MC CRAIG, DONALD**

Title ——— Rural Firemen. | il | Country Journal | 16 | : | 79–83 ——— Pages

Illustrated ——— Volume

Date ——— Mr/Ap '89 ——— Magazine

1. Who wrote the article "Edible Flowers"? _____

2. In what magazine will you find the article "Rural Firemen"? _____

3. Who is the author of "Rural Firemen"? _____

4. In what magazine will you find the article "Edible Flowers"? _____

5. Under what subject entry might you find the article "Rural Firemen"? _____

6. On what pages will you find the article "Rural Firemen"? _____

7. In what volume of <u>Country Journal</u> does "Rural Firemen" appear? _____

8. In what month and year was "Edible Flowers" published? _____

9. What abbreviation is used for the word <u>illustrated</u>? _____

10. In what month and year was "Rural Firemen" published? _____

Choosing Reference Sources

85

- Use a **dictionary** to find the definitions of words and pronunciations of words, suggestions for word usage, and etymologies.
- Use an **encyclopedia** to find articles about many different people, places, and other subjects. Use an encyclopedia to find references to related subjects.
- Use a **thesaurus** to find synonyms and antonyms.
- Use the *Readers' Guide to Periodical Literature* to find magazine articles on specific subjects or by particular authors.
- Use an **atlas** to find maps and other information about geographical locations.
- Use an **almanac,** an annual publication, to find such information as population numbers, annual rainfall, election statistics, and other specific information for a given year.

- Write <u>dictionary</u>, <u>encyclopedia</u>, <u>thesaurus</u>, *Readers' Guide*, <u>atlas</u>, or <u>almanac</u> to show where you would find the following information. Some information may be found in more than one source.

_____ **1.** the life of George Washington

_____ **2.** an article on the latest space-shuttle flight

_____ **3.** the states through which the Rocky Mountains run

_____ **4.** the origin of the word <u>tomato</u>

_____ **5.** the annual rainfall for the state of Maryland

_____ **6.** the most direct route from California to New York

_____ **7.** an antonym for the word <u>happy</u>

_____ **8.** the meaning of the word <u>spar</u>

_____ **9.** recent articles written on the subject of air pollution

_____ **10.** the pronunciation of the word <u>wren</u>

_____ **11.** the life of Thomas Jefferson

_____ **12.** a synonym for the word <u>bad</u>

_____ **13.** the years during which the Revolutionary War was fought

_____ **14.** an article on rock climbing

_____ **15.** the final standings of the National Football League for last year

_____ **16.** the meaning of the word <u>history</u>

> ■ Use reference sources—dictionaries, encyclopedias, the *Readers' Guide to Periodical Literature,* thesauruses, atlases, and almanacs—to find information about people, places, or things with which you are not familiar. You can also use these sources to find out more about subjects that interest you.

A. Follow the directions below.

1. Choose a person from history that you would like to know more about.

Person's name: _____

2. Name two reference sources that you can use to find information about this person.

a. _____

b. _____

3. Use one of the reference sources you named above. Find the entry for the person you are researching. Write the exact title of the reference.

_____

4. Write a short summary of the information you found.

_____

_____

_____

_____

5. Name the source that would contain recent articles about this person.

_____

6. Look up your person's name in the reference source you listed in number 5. Write the titles of three articles that were listed.

a. _____

b. _____

c. _____

7. Which articles above, if any, can be found in your library?

_____

8. Name a subject heading under which you might find more information on your person.

_____

B. Follow the directions, and answer the questions.

1. Choose a country you would like to know more about.

   Name of country: _____

2. List four reference sources that you can use to find information about this country.

   a. _____   c. _____

   b. _____   d. _____

3. Find the entry for the country in one of the reference sources you listed.
   Write the exact title of the reference source.

   _____

4. Write a short summary of the information you found.

   _____

   _____

   _____

   _____

5. Find the entry for the country in one other reference source. Write the exact
   title of the reference source.

   _____

6. What new information did you find about the country?

   _____

   _____

   _____

C. Follow the directions, and answer the questions below.

1. In what state do you live? _____

2. Find the entry for your state in one of the reference sources. Write the exact

   title of the reference source. _____

3. Write a short summary of the information you found about your state.

   _____

   _____

   _____

   _____

A. Use the dictionary samples below to answer the questions.

ex-pose (eks pōz′) *v.* **1.** to leave open to external influence: *He was exposed to the measles.* **2.** to make known. **3.** to permit light to reach, as in photography. [Middle English *exposen,* from Middle French *exposer,* from Latin *exponere* to set forth, explain.]

ex-po-si-tion (eks pə zish′ ən) *n.* **1.** a large public display. **2.** the act of explaining ideas or facts.

ex-press (eks pres′) *v.* **1.** to put into words: *Tom always wants to express his views.* **2.** to show outwardly:

Her face expressed sadness. **3.** to send something quickly: *They expressed the package overnight.* [Middle English, from Middle French *expres,* from Latin *expressus* to press out, express.]

ex-qui-site (eks kwiz′ it) *adj.* **1.** of great beauty: *The exquisite sculpture was put on display.* **2.** of extremely high quality. *The exquisite necklace was one of a kind.* [Middle English, from Latin *exquisitus* from *exquirere* to search out, from *ex* + *quaerere* to seek.]

1. Underline the words that could be guide words for the dictionary page above.

   a. expel / expire   **c.** export / extend

   b. expand / expense   **d.** extra / extreme

2. What part of speech is <u>expose</u>? _____ <u>exposition</u>? _____ <u>express</u>? _____

3. How many syllables does the word <u>exposition</u> have? _____ <u>express</u>? _____

4. Write the correct word for each respelling.

   a. (eks kwiz′ it) _____   **c.** (eks pə zish′ ən) _____

   b. (eks pōz′) _____   **d.** (eks pres′) _____

5. What word comes from the Latin word <u>expressus</u>? _____

6. From what three languages does the word <u>expose</u> come?

   _____   _____   _____

7. Write one sentence in which you use <u>express</u> according to its second definition.

   _____

8. What word comes from a Latin word that means "to search out"? _____

B. Write <u>title page</u>, <u>copyright page</u>, <u>table of contents</u>, or <u>index</u> to tell where to find this information.

_____   **1.** the author's name

_____   **2.** the chapter titles

_____   **3.** the year the book was published

_____   **4.** the page number on which a particular topic can be found

_____   **5.** the publisher's name

_____   **6.** the book's title

A. Find the word <u>humor</u> in your dictionary. Then follow the directions and answer the questions.

1. Write the guide words from the page on which you found the entry for <u>humor</u>. _____

2. Write <u>humor</u> in syllables. _____

3. As what parts of speech can <u>humor</u> be used? _____

4. Write the history of the word. _____

_____

B. Use the sample catalog card to answer the questions.

> 971.3
>
> **Jackson, Taylor**
>   Life in the colonies: the story of day-to-day life in colonial America told through the eyes of the young Taylor Jackson. New York, Colonial Press [1972]   130 p.   illus.

1. What type of catalog card is this?

   a. subject card   **b.** author card   **c.** title card

2. Who is the author of the book? _____

3. What is the title of the book? _____

4. Is the book illustrated? _____

C. Use the encyclopedia sample to answer the questions.

> **CREE** is the name of a North American Indian tribe now living on reservations in Canada. They were originally forest hunters and trappers who traded with the early French and English fur traders. Part of the tribe moved southwest into buffalo country and became known as Plaines Cree. *See also* AMERICAN INDIANS.

1. What is the article about? _____

2. Where did some members of the tribe move? _____

3. Under what subject heading can you find related information?

_____

D. Use the *Readers' Guide* sample to answer the questions.

> **FITZPATRICK, JEAN GRASSO**
> How to slow down. il Parents 64:97–102 Ap '89

1. What is the title of the article? _____

2. Who is the author? _____

3. In what magazine does the article appear? _____

4. On what pages will you find the article? _____

E. Use a thesaurus to find a synonym for each underlined word.

_____ 1. My milk shake was so <u>large</u> that I couldn't finish it.

_____ 2. The police <u>found</u> our stolen property.

_____ 3. There are a lot of <u>old</u> ruins in Greece and Italy.

F. Use the information in the chart to complete the graph. Then answer the questions.

Club Membership

Chart

Year	Men	Women
1950	40	20
1960	20	40
1970	30	10
1980	20	30

Graph

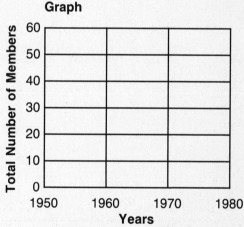

1. How many women belonged to the club in 1960? _____

2. What was the total number of members in 1960? _____

3. What two years had an equal number of members? _____

4. Which year had the lowest number of members? _____

Synonyms, Antonyms, Homonyms, and Homographs ▪ On the line before each pair of words, write <u>S</u> if they are synonyms, <u>A</u> if they are antonyms, <u>H</u> if they are homonyms, and <u>HG</u> if they are homographs.

1. _____ brave, courageous

2. _____ plane, plain

3. _____ to, two

4. _____ start, commence

5. _____ bark, bark

6. _____ happy, unhappy

7. _____ late, early

8. _____ desert, desert

9. _____ smile, grin

10. _____ there, their

11. _____ quick, slow

12. _____ capital, capitol

13. _____ arm, arm

14. _____ begin, end

15. _____ country, nation

Prefixes, Suffixes, and Compound Words ▪ Write <u>P</u> if the underlined word has a prefix, write <u>S</u> if it has a suffix, and write <u>C</u> if it is a compound word.

1. _____ _____ Tony was <u>careful</u> as he walked <u>uphill</u> to the playing field.

2. _____ _____ It seemed awfully wet for the <u>softball</u> game. He was not <u>hopeful</u>.

3. _____ _____ He began to <u>rethink</u> his decision to play. Perhaps he had been <u>foolish</u>.

4. _____ _____ His <u>teammates</u> would be <u>helpless</u> in this mud.

5. _____ _____ The other team felt <u>unhappy</u>. They said running could be <u>hazardous</u>.

6. _____ _____ Suddenly there was a <u>downpour</u>. They would be <u>unable</u> to play.

Contractions ▪ Write the contraction for each pair of words.

1. I am _____

2. would not _____

3. do not _____

4. I have _____

5. you have _____

6. is not _____

7. will not _____

8. does not _____

9. I will _____

10. they are _____

11. had not _____

12. there is _____

Connotation, Denotation, Idioms ▪ For each underlined word or words, write (–) for a negative connotation, (+) for a positive connotation, or (N) for a neutral connotation. Write <u>I</u> if the words make an idiom.

1. _____ Jake told us a <u>story</u> at the party.

2. _____ Jake is such a <u>showoff</u>.

3. _____ He <u>brags</u> about his sense of humor.

4. _____ Often he tells a <u>hilarious</u> story.

5. _____ This story didn't <u>knock my socks off</u>.

6. _____ In fact, I got <u>bored</u>, so I left.

7. _____ I went home and fell <u>asleep</u>.

8. _____ Actually, I went <u>out like a light</u>.

9. _____ Sue <u>giggled</u> at the joke.

10. _____ She <u>wept</u> at the last act.

11. _____ He can <u>fly like a bird</u>.

12. _____ His smile <u>lit up the sky</u>.

13. _____ Suddenly he <u>snarled</u>.

14. _____ The <u>curtain came down</u>.

15. _____ We <u>plodded</u> home.

16. _____ We ate <u>delicious</u> muffins.

Types of Sentences ▪ Before each sentence, write D for declarative, IN for interrogative, IM for imperative, and E for exclamatory. Punctuate each sentence correctly.

1. _____ Oh, the road is closed____

2. _____ What should we do now____

3. _____ Stop talking and let me think____

4. _____ We must find a new road____

5. _____ I'll pull over to the side of the road____

6. _____ Get the map that's on the backseat____

7. _____ Which is the best road____

8. _____ I'll never find an alternate route____

Parts of a Sentence ▪ Underline the word or words in each sentence that are identified in parentheses.

1. (compound predicate)   Steve washed and waxed his car.

2. (indirect object)   I'm sure Steve will give you a ride when he is finished.

3. (simple subject)   The sky-blue car shone in the sun.

4. (direct object)   Steve loved his car.

5. (subordinate clause)   The manual that he received with the car gave lots of information.

6. (complete predicate)   Steve has read the entire manual.

7. (complete subject)   Steve's brothers help him wash the car.

8. (simple predicate)   Steve has kept his car in good condition.

9. (independent clause)   Steve's neighbor helps Steve since he wants to become a mechanic.

10. (compound subject)   Steve and his brothers will take turns driving the car on their vacation.

Compound Sentences ▪ Combine each pair of sentences below to form a compound sentence.

1. Jason wasn't sure what to do. Maria wasn't helping with her suggestions.

_____

2. He listened to what Susan said. Her ideas just wouldn't work.

_____

3. It was getting dark. They needed to leave soon.

_____

4. Jason had an idea. Maria agreed with the idea.

_____

Correcting Run-on Sentences and Expanding Sentences ▪ Correct the run-on sentence. Then expand each new sentence by adding details.

Lee ran down the track, he was in the lead.

1. _____

2. _____

Grammar and Usage ▪ **Fill in the blanks by supplying the word or words specified in parentheses.**

Manatees _____ mammals whose population is endangered. Also
(linking verb)

known as Sea Cows, manatees have dark gray skin, a very small head, poorly developed

eyes that _____ see _____, and two front
(contraction of do)   (adverb)

flippers. _____ tails are large, rounded flippers. Manatees live
(possessive pronoun)

_____ shallow, fresh water or saltwater and eat underwater plants.
(preposition)

They _____ in the southeastern part _____
(intransitive verb)   (preposition)

the United States, western Africa, South America, the Amazon, and the Caribbean Sea.

Manatees are _____ gentle animals. _____
(adverb)   (gerund of rub)

muzzles is how they communicate. If alarmed, _____ make a
(subject pronoun)

_____ noise. By adulthood, they grow to between eight and fifteen feet
(present participle of chirp)

_____ weigh _____ 1,500 pounds. Scientists
(conjunction)   (adverb)

studying _____ adult manatee _____ observed
(limiting adjective)   (helping verb)

that it can eat about 100 pounds of plants in one day.

Manatees _____ clean waterways by eating vegetation before it blocks
(helping verb)

narrow passages. In some areas, manatees are encouraged _____,
(infinitive of thrive)

so they _____ waterways free of plants. Boats and boat propellers
(future tense of keep)

are the _____ enemy of the manatee. In a few places, people hunt
(superlative adjective)

_____ for meat, oil, and hides. _____
(object pronoun)   (demonstrative adjective)

hunting has led to the decline of the manatee population. _____,
(conjunction)

in most areas, manatees _____ by law.
(protect in passive voice)

Capitalization and End Punctuation ▪ Circle each letter that should be capitalized.
Write the capital letter above it. Add correct end punctuation to each sentence.

1. the road rally will start on nov. 1 in detroit, michigan____

2. tom asked, "how many italian sports cars will be entered____"

3. dr. smith plans to enter betsy, his antique ford____

4. "wow, betsy is the best american car in the rally!" said mr. lane____

5. they heard there might be a special entry from japan____

6. tom asked, "are you sure the entry arrived before the deadline on monday____"

7. mr lane said, "no, but i did see an address from kyoto, japan, with the list of competitors____"

8. "betsy will have no trouble beating the competition," said tom____

9. "wasn't she named car of the year in 1910 by *auto journal*?" asked ms. cronin____

10. tom exclaimed, "you're absolutely right____"

Punctuation and Capitalization ▪ Circle each letter that should be capitalized below.
Add commas, question marks, quotation marks, apostrophes, periods, colons, and
hyphens where needed.

3720 w. anderson
phoenix, az 37825
may 7, 1990

ms. jean jackson
735 w. 79th street
detroit, mi 14728

Dear ms. jackson

   i want to enter my antique ford betsy in the Rally of the Americas to be held
august 12, 1990____ please send me any information i may need to register____ i
understand you only accept seventy five entries____ am i too late____ i was told to
wait until may to inquire so i hope there are still openings____

   a friend who has entered in the past said this is the best rally of the whole
year____ im excited about entering____ my car is a 1910 classic in excellent
condition____ it has won numerous awards over the years and it is not ready to
retire____ my wife and i are looking forward to the drive from our home in arizona
all the way to detroit____ were studying the book *the motor city* in anticipation of
our visit____ ill be waiting to hear from you____

Sincerely yours,
dr. lee smith

Composition ▪ **Read the paragraphs. Then answer the questions that follow.**

In order to prove that shipwrecked sailors could survive in an open boat at sea, Dr. Bombard decided to conduct an experiment. First, he chose a 15-foot open rubber boat. Then he decided not to take any food or water with him. Since most shipwrecked sailors die from lack of food or water, he wanted to find a way to survive strictly off the sea. Finally, on October 19, 1953, Dr. Bombard started his journey across the Atlantic Ocean.

Dr. Bombard discovered two very important things on his journey. The most important was that sailors could drink seawater. This was something that many felt would speed death instead of helping people to live. Dr. Bombard drank over a pint of seawater every day and lived to tell about it. His next important discovery was that he could keep from getting diseases caused by lack of proper vitamins by eating plankton. Plankton are small, vitamin-rich plants and animals that float in the sea. Many sea creatures live on plankton. Eating just a teaspoon or so of plankton a day gave him all the vitamins and minerals he needed. He also ate raw fish that he caught daily. Although he lost 56 pounds, Dr. Bombard proved that sailors could survive by living off the sea.

1. Underline the topic sentence in each paragraph.

2. How many supporting details are in the first paragraph? _____ in the second? _____

3. Is the first paragraph written in chronological order or spatial order? _____

4. Write the time order words found in the first paragraph.

_____   _____   _____

5. What is the topic of the selection? _____

6. Write one possible audience that might be interested in the selection.

_____

7. Complete the outline for the selection.

I. Dr. Bombard gets ready

  A. _____

  B. _____

II. Discoveries

  A. _____

  B. _____

8. Write two questions you would ask Dr. Bombard in an interview.

  a. _____

  b. _____

Using the Dictionary ▪ Use the dictionary samples to answer the questions.

earn (ûrn) *v.* **1.** to receive in return for work done. **2.** To become deserving or worthy; *Nancy earned first place in the tournament.* [Middle English *ernen*, from Old English *earnian*]

earth (ûrth) *n.* **1.** The third planet from the sun. **2.** The dry land of the planet. **3.** Soft, loose, dirt suitable for planting. [Middle English *erthe*, from Old English *eorthe*, related to Old High German *erda*, earth, from Greek *eraze* to the ground]

1. Circle the letter of the guide words for the above entry.

    a. east / ebb   **b.** each / easily   **c.** each / eagle

2. How many definitions are listed for earn? _____ earth? _____

3. Write one sentence using the second definition of earth.

_____

4. Write the most commonly used definition of earn. _____

_____

5. What part of speech is earn? _____ earth? _____

6. How many syllables do earn and earth have? _____

7. Write the respelling of earn. _____ earth. _____

8. Which word came from the Old English word earnian? _____

9. Which word means the same in Old High German as it does in modern English? _____

Parts of a Book ▪ Write title page, copyright page, table of contents, or index to tell where you would find this information.

_____ **1.** The page on which specific information can be found

_____ **2.** The author's name

_____ **3.** The page on which a chapter begins

_____ **4.** The year the book was published

Reference Sources ▪ Write D for dictionary, E for encyclopedia, TH for thesaurus, AL for almanac, AT for atlas, or RG for *Readers' Guide* to tell where you would find this information.

_____ **1.** an article on the New York Mets

_____ **2.** the etymology of the word baseball

_____ **3.** the history of the Red Cross

_____ **4.** the distance between Rome and Naples

_____ **5.** a synonym for the word build

_____ **6.** planning a vegetable garden